THE ELEMENT

THE ELEMENTS
OF DOWSING

BY

LE VICOMTE HENRY DE FRANCE

TRANSLATED BY
A. H. BELL

LONDON
G. BELL & SONS LTD
1977

First published in 1948 by
G. Bell & Sons Ltd
York House, 6 Portugal Street,
London WC2A 2HL

Reprinted 1951, 1959,
1967, 1971, 1977

ISBN 0 7135 0246 0

Printed in Great Britain by
The Camelot Press Ltd, Southampton

CONTENTS

		PAGE
Foreword	. . . .	vii
Introduction	. . . . . .	ix

I. History of the Art of Dowsing . . . 1

II. Pendulum and Rod 4
The pendulum—Holding and adjustment of the pendulum—What it is we perceive—The causes of the pendulum's movements—The rod—Definitions.

III. General Technique 14
Method of fields—Methods of check and identification—Electrical radiesthesia—Use of the rod—The method of samples—The meridian and solar planes—Means of control—The method of series—Some useful series—The method of colours.

IV. Dowsing for Water 29
Wells and springs—Locating a stream—Yield—Depth—Potability—Streams and fissures—Hot and mineral springs—Automatic adjustment of the pendulum—Ascending waters—The rod and Mr. Maby's experiments.

V. Dowsing for Minerals and Metals . . . 39
Identification of specimens—Analysing a specimen—Prospection for veins and masses—Cavities, valuables, coal and oil.

VI. Alimentary Radiesthesia 45
Technique: Coefficients and measurements—Choice of food—Cooking.

PAGE

VII. Medical Radiesthesia 51
Diagnosis—Human products—Remedies—Injurious rays.

VIII. Agricultural Radiesthesia 57
Application of the method of fields—Application of the
method of samples—Manures—Accords—Application of
the method of series—Application of the method of
colours—Drainage.

IX. Teleradiesthesia or Superpendulism . . 65

Index 81

EQUIVALENTS

1 Metre	=	39·37 inches
1 Centimetre	=	·39 (about $\frac{2}{5}$) inch
1 Foot	=	30·48 centimetres
1 Inch	=	2·54 centimetres

*   *   *

1 pound avoirdupois	=	453·6 grams
100 grams	=	3·53 ounces

FOREWORD

TO the great regret of all who knew him, the author of this little book, Vicomte Henry de France, has not lived to see its appearance, for he died last year, on June 23rd, 1947, at Chateau d'Arry, his ancestral home.

The information he has given repeats to some extent that contained in *The Modern Dowser*, which was a translation of *Le Sourcier Moderne*, now in its ninth edition, but it includes much new advice on the study and testing of foods, and an interesting chapter on the purely divinatory aspect of dowsing known in France as *Téléradesthésie*.

A welcome feature in his instruction is its freedom from complicated refinements and a lack of the misleading use of words and expressions which possess specialist meanings for the physicist.

Unlike certain authors, M. de France has not attempted to ascribe a physical basis to the undoubted facts of Teleradesthesia, but has wisely referred them to the psychic sphere, which had for him no attraction.

It is to be hoped that this book will prove a useful guide to all who intend to develop and interpret the reflexes resulting from their sensitiveness to radiation, and that they will derive much benefit from this valuable addition to their other senses.

A. H. B.

INTRODUCTION

IT is as well that I should give my reasons for writing a new book in place of a revision of *The Modern Dowser*, the last edition of which, published in 1936, is now exhausted.

During the last ten years Radiesthesia has made such progress that it would have been necessary to recast the old book anew in order to include recent discoveries and to eliminate a number of mistaken conceptions.

Moreover, the method previously described has undergone profound modifications which tend to make it more accessible to the general public. It has been subjected to a searching scrutiny, from which it has emerged in a very different form from that it held originally.

I have not considered it necessary in this new book to give so much space to the history of Radiesthesia, in which only a few dowsers would be interested. A full record of the origins of our art will be found in *The Divining Rod*, by Sir William Barrett and Theodore Besterman; *Water Divining*, by Theodore Besterman; *Water Diviners and their Methods* (a translation of *Les Sourciers et Leurs Procédés* by H. Mager), and in *The Physics of the Divining Rod*, by J. C. Maby and T. B. Franklin.

I have omitted all the previous references to Geology and Mineralogy, not because I consider them useless, but because, being incomplete, they might tend to mislead dowsers who need a profound knowledge of these sciences when undertaking work of an important or expensive nature.

On the other hand, I have dwelt on Radiesthesia in its application to 'foods' at some length, a branch of our art barely thought of ten years ago, but one which is accessible to all without demanding any special knowledge. In much the same category is Radiesthesia as applied to agriculture; this has undergone some important developments, and should be of great service in these times of poor nourishment.

Finally, in these latter years a new use of the pendulum has arisen which, by reason of its divinatory application, seems to distinguish it more and more from Radiesthesia in the true sense of the word. It is variously called Teleradiesthesia, Divinatory Pendulism, Superpendulism, and so on. It started from work on plans and photos, and has gradually been extended to all sorts of inquiry, answers to questions being revealed by indications of the pendulum. I have tried my best to define what this novel use embraces and in what way it differs from the familiar one. I hope thus to stop the confusion which has been growing during the last few years between these two applications of the pendulum, the instrument most frequently used to-day. I am sure that this distinction will be welcomed by operators of both kinds.

The elementary method of Radiesthesia properly so called, which I am now expounding, has been matured by more than twenty years' experience; it is one easy to learn quickly and within the reach of all.

If this method, which is far from being of a personal nature, but is compounded of those of the best-known dowsers, were adopted by the generality of Radiesthetists to-day, there would be an end to the reproach so often urged by scientists against our art, that it is lacking in uniformity of presentation.

I would strongly recommend those of my readers who are new to dowsing to begin with a study of Radiesthesia as applied to foods. Most of them will find an immediate and really useful field of application for it in their daily life, one which affects very closely both themselves and their neighbours. I should add that Radiesthesia of Foods is that which can be learnt and put to use most easily and quickly. In fact it is enough to know how to adjust the pendulum, and then one can pass at once to experiments of the greatest interest. Having acquired the habit of using the pendulum at every meal, the novice will easily proceed to other uses of his instrument, and will become more and more convinced of the large range of objects to which it can be applied.

HENRY DE FRANCE

CHAPTER I

HISTORY OF THE ART OF DOWSING

THE art of dowsing, or Radiesthesia, goes back to the most remote antiquity, and is found more or less mixed up with magical practices and superstitions in all parts of the world. It was used almost exclusively in the search for water and minerals, the only instrument then being the rod, a springy arrangement made of two bits of wood, joined naturally or artificially.

Though referred to by authors previous to the seventeenth century, it was only at the beginning of that period that our art made its official appearance in history with the Baron and Baroness de Beausoleil, both renowned mineralogists. Jean du Chastelet, Baron de Beausoleil, had travelled in Germany and Hungary. He had noticed that miners in those countries used the rod with success. He became Lieut.-General of Mines in France, and his wife produced in 1630 *La Véritable Déclaration des Mines de France*, and in 1640 *La Restitution de Pluton*. Implicated in the conspiracy of St. Mars, they were both imprisoned, and before long departed this life, one in the Bastille and the other at Vincennes (cf. Riboulet, *La Découverte des eaux minérales de Château-Thierry*. Harvich, Château-Thierry, 1930). Their son succeeded his father as Lieut.-General of Mines. The Beausoleils discovered most of the mines which were developed in France then and afterwards. Their successes were responsible for the appearance of a number of books during the seventeenth century, of which the best known is that of the Abbé of Vallemont, *La Physique Occulte ou Traité de la Baguette Divinatoire*. The Abbé connects the dowser's art with the physical theories of Descartes, and describes the methods then in use—those of 'fields' and 'samples', which are the most important of those used at the present time.

In 1750 an English engineer of German origin, Diederich Wessel Linden, published *Three Letters on Mining and Smelting*, dedicated to Lord Halifax; it was translated into French shortly after. He seems to have been the first to connect dowsing with electricity, on which discussion was just beginning. This theme was further developed by De Thouvenel in 1781 in his *Mémoire physique et médicinal, montrant des rapports évidents entre les phénomènes de la Baguette Divinatoire, du Magnétisme et de l'Électricité*.

At the beginning of the nineteenth century, Gerboin, Professor at the Faculty of Medicine at Strasbourg, made a study of the pendulum and wrote a book about the movements of this instrument over masses of metal. About the same time Ritter, a well-known German physicist, published a book on the same subject.

Ampère and Chevreul, who are reckoned amongst the greatest of French scientists, repeated their experiments, and published their criticisms in the *Revue des Deux Mondes* of May 1833, ("Letter to Ampère on a peculiar class of muscular movements.")

Chevreul, as a check on his experiments, had adopted the method of 'eyes closed', to which he quite correctly attached decisive importance, but, in so far as he tried it, he obtained only negative results. He did not realise the possibility of 'adjusting' the pendulum (see p. 7).

During the whole of the nineteenth century but few books were published on the art of dowsing, one of them being that of the Comte de Tristan, who also connected our art with electricity.

According to his unpublished papers, to which I have had access, Comte de Tristan appears to be the first to have entertained the idea of using the rod for medical purposes. He describes in a letter how with his rod he was able to find a remedy for a case of facial neuralgia.

The art of dowsing had been almost forgotten in France when, in 1913, M. Henri Mager, a colonial journalist and author of books on hydrology, and M. Armand Viré, Director of the laboratory at the Museum, had the idea of taking advantage of a Congress of Experimental Psychology to collect a few of the local dowsers to be found here and there in our countryside, and organise a meeting with tests of a practical kind. This happy idea proved a great success. After the war of 1914 the movement thus begun underwent a vigorous revival as remarkable as it was unexpected. This was mainly due to two French ecclesiastics, the Abbés Bouly and Mermet, who organised a series of prospections and conferences. Moreover, they extended very considerably the applications of the rod and the pendulum, notably in the medical field, where they soon achieved remarkable success. In 1930 Abbé Bouly invented the word *Radiesthésie*, which has been universally adopted as the designation of our art. Shortly afterwards began our International Congresses, which were held regularly until the outbreak of the late war, the last taking place at Liége in 1939.

In the meantime our great Societies were founded, L'Association des Amis de la Radiesthésie in 1930, followed by the British Society of Dowsers in 1933. Other Societies of the same type were started in Western Europe. The British Society was the only one to continue its activities during the war.

At the present time there is a general reviv: l of activity, which, we may hope, will soon attain the intensity which characterised it before the war from which we have lately emerged.

CHAPTER II

PENDULUM AND ROD

ALTHOUGH the pendulum is not so old as the rod in the history of our art, we will discuss it first because nowadays it is more generally used amongst radiesthetists than is the rod. The pendulum is more convenient to handle, as it requires the use of only one hand, and is better suited for certain kinds of work. Moreover, I believe everyone can learn to use the one instrument as aptly as the other, and it is well to know how to employ each for the purpose for which it is best suited.

THE PENDULUM

How to Make it

Take a wooden ball or cylinder weighing from 20 to 50 grams (0·7 to 1·76 oz.) or more—a heavy pendulum is preferable for beginners —then a length of 25 cm. (10 inches) of pliant and strong thread ending in a loop. Make a hole in the ball and fix the loop in the hole by means of a small wooden peg. Fasten the thread to a little stick about 10 cm.

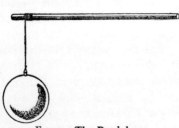

Fig. 1. The Pendulum.

(4 inches) long and 3 to 4 mm. thick, and wind up the thread on it near one end. Pendulums are usually painted black. Other materials than wood, such as glass or other non-conductors of electricity, can be used. Metals are not suitable, for, as we shall see later, they can act as 'sam-

4

ples' and produce special effects. It is for this reason that it is often said that the pendulum should be 'neutral'.

You can also make what is called a 'hollow' pendulum. It consists essentially of a little receptacle of earthenware or of wood with a string handle to which the thread is fastened. We shall learn the peculiar uses of this pendulum later. If used for general purposes its weight can be altered by putting in it bits of metal wrapped in paper or other insulating material. Certain operators advocate solid pendu-

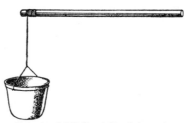

FIG. 2. A 'Hollow' Pendulum.

lums containing some special substance inside, but I have not found anything in this idea. We will revert to this question later when we discuss automatic adjustment of the pendulum.

I cannot recommend too strongly that radiesthetists should from the start make a practice of manufacturing

FIG. 3. A Device for Easy Transport.

their own instruments. It can be done easily and cheaply, and, moreover, has the great advantage of providing an instrument exactly fitted to the various ends required; it cannot but make the study of Radiesthesia more attractive.

Handling and Adjustment of the Pendulum

Take the pendulum by the little stick and hold it over any object at choice. Swing it and impress yourself with your *intention* that it should gyrate; it will forthwith quit the plane of oscillation and begin to gyrate. This is a fact well known to Experimental Psychology, and has nothing to do with Radiesthesia. It is, however, well to remember it, for many beginners wrongly imagine that they will never get their pendulum to gyrate.

Your swinging pendulum has started to gyrate, but while it is doing so shut your eyes (thereby repeating the experiment of Ampère and Chevreul). When you open them you will see that the gyration has ceased and that the pendulum is again oscillating. In making this experiment it is well to use a light pendulum, so that you may not notice the effect of the varying movements on your hand.

The fact that the nature of the movement has changed is a sign that the movement was due to yourself, and not to an external cause. Evidently such a discovery is nothing to be pleased about. You have made your pendulum gyrate, and without muscular effort, which is something, but after having shut your eyes you found that the movement of gyration did not continue, showing that it was the result of autosuggestion, and therefore had no objective significance.

I must admit that I have met people who have stated that in their case shutting the eyes in no way disturbed the pendulum's gyration. I think, however, that this is accounted for by the fact that they foresee the possible change, and so more or less consciously maintain the original state of movement. However that may be, it must be accepted that, generally speaking, closing the eyes when the string of the pendulum is held at no particular point leads to a cessation of the gyrating movement and to a return of oscillation.

What can we do in the face of this rather discouraging observation—one well calculated to destroy a beginner's confidence? Unless one is endowed with the genius of Divination, one cannot claim that a movement due entirely to yourself can be of any scientific interest.

The answer to this question appears to be as follows: We have been discussing a pendulum of which the string was grasped at *any* point. Let us see what happens if we select a special point at which to hold it—and thereby 'adjust' the pendulum.

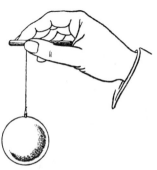

FIG. 4. How to Hold the Pendulum.

To do this, grasp the little stick by the end on which the thread is wound between the thumb and first finger, so that the string passes between them when you twist the stick round, the other end of the little stick resting against the base of the little finger.

Place the object of study below the hand holding the pendulum and wind up the thread on the little stick almost entirely. Now slowly unwind the thread, at the same time swinging the pendulum with some force to the right and left. After unwinding a certain length you will notice that the pendulum deviates slightly from the original plane of oscillation, indicating a tendency to gyrate. Don't oppose this movement, rather encourage it. Of course, as soon as the deviation begins, stop unwinding the thread. The pendulum is then adjusted.

Later on, when you are more practised, you will not

have to encourage the movement, the pendulum will gyrate of its own accord. At the start you can, for convenience sake, unwind the thread with both hands, and, when it gyrates, hold it in one hand as already described.

You can adjust the pendulum in the same manner at short distances, pointing the left hand at the object with the arm extended.

You will notice that your pendulum, so adjusted, stands up perfectly to the test of 'eyes closed' and continues to gyrate. And so, whereas in the case of the pendulum with the thread held at any length the change of movement appeared to be due to a subjective cause, you are now justified in believing that the gyration of your pendulum is an objective phenomenon. You are therefore working under the normal and usual conditions of scientific research.

You have yet other methods of check to verify whether the gyration is due to an external cause.

The first is the immediate transfer of the gyrating pendulum to another object. Experience will show that your pendulum with the same length of thread will not gyrate over *any other* object, as can be well understood. But if, instead, you transfer the pendulum to over your left hand (as being a part of the human body) you will find that sometimes it will continue to gyrate, but at other times will pass to oscillation. In the first case the adjustment was bad, and in the second case good.

Another method consists in making a long and continuous exhalation whilst the pendulum is gyrating—an excellent exercise for emptying the lungs of carbonic acid. If the pendulum changes to oscillation you must correct your adjustment or give up the experiment.

A fourth method consists in taking a pointed object, such as a safety-pin, and pointing it with the left hand towards the object. If the gyration is modified, proceed as before.

These two latter checks are not as good as the first two. In fact, they can be looked upon as experiments, useful for eliminating minor influences, but one cannot say that they are decisive in discriminating between the objective and the subjective as are the first two.

What it is We Perceive ?

Beginners are recommended to experiment at first on objects which are magnetised or electrified, bodies at a high temperature or naturally radioactive, magnets, glass and wax when rubbed, electric currents, coal or wood fires. They can then pass on to metals, soils, plants, animals and the human body.

As regards the first set of objects, there can be no doubt about the nature of what we perceive—namely their outstanding magnetic, electric, calorific or radioactive physical properties—but regarding the other category the answer is not so easy. One might say that it is a question of modification in the terrestrial magnetic field of which the lines of force undergo more or less rapid variation according to the permeability of each object. We will see later that Mr. J. Cecil Maby has adopted an entirely new line of research, in that he checks the dowser's indications with laboratory instruments, thereby ascertaining the nature of the physical influence involved.

Causes of the Pendulum's Movements

The pendulum gyrates, simply because the hand makes it do so.

It is easy to see that this is so by watching carefully any dowser at work. You can observe the same phenomenon by advancing towards an object which causes strong reactions, such as a source of heat, a magnet, an electric current, etc., moving the *empty* clenched fist backwards and forwards the while. When you get near the object your fist will start a circular movement after an interval more or less long; this varies with the individual, but is always apparent in the end. It is evident that if you had been carrying a pendulum it would have taken up the circular movement. I always recommend beginners to practise this exercise, as it is an excellent one for making the muscles of the arms supple, and is a good preparation for work with the pendulum.

THE ROD

The rod is made of two round bits of springy wood (hazel, willow, osier, etc.), 25 to 30 cm. (10 to 12 inches) long, as alike as possible, or else of two flat bits of whalebone, which, on the whole, is preferable. The ends of the two sticks are tied tightly together. If you are afraid of the sticks breaking, which happens sometimes, you can use two bits of steel, but they should be sheathed in leather or some kind of insulating material, as in the case of the metal pendulum. The preliminary exercise without an instrument is particularly useful in the case of the rod.

Clench both your fists and, with arms bent at the elbows and moving the fists quickly to and from each other, go forward as already described towards an object causing strong reactions.

When you reach the object you will see that one of your fists is not at the same level as the other, seeming to want to pass a little above or below it when they approach each other; a movement which is accentuated when a 'sample' is carried (see p. 19).

Now take your rod in the palms of your hands, nails

upwards if the branches are round and stiff; between the thumb and the ends of the first three fingers, if the branches are flat. In either case the rod should be as nearly horizontal as possible, with the point in front.

The rod can also be held with the point towards the body, with the back of the hand upwards; being well wedged in the hands, it keeps its horizontal position better. It will dip over positive, and rise over negative electricity.

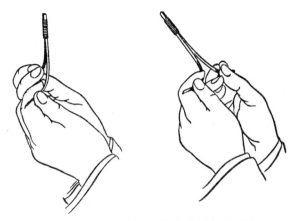

FIG. 5. A Delicate Whalebone Rod Held in the Fingers.

Some dowsers prefer a very light rod made of short strips of whalebone as they find it responds more easily and is less tiring to use.

When you walk above the object, the involuntary movement of the hands will make the rod swing upwards or downwards.

You can carry out exactly the same experiments with the rod as with the pendulum. However, the methods of check by means of the 'eyes closed' and so on can hardly be applied to the preliminary exercise we have described.

Later on, when we get to more complicated experiments, we will describe how the movements of the rod can be checked.

DEFINITIONS

The word *Radiesthésie*, introduced by Abbé Bouly in 1930, exactly represents etymologically, 'Sensation of Radiation', and one might include 'other physical effects'. In this definition the word 'Sensation' is all-important. It belongs to Psychology and its use implies that Radiesthesia obeys the three well-known laws of Sensation we read of in manuals of Philosophy, the law of Upper and Lower Limits, of Range and of Relativity.

What we have said above about the handling of our instruments shows that the motor sensations of the hands are involved—in other words, an extension of the sense of Touch exerted at short range. Indeed, there is no valid reason for supposing that the sense of Touch working through the motor sensations should be in the enjoyment of extraordinary privileges in the matter of range which are denied to the senses of Sight and Hearing.

Investigations in Radiesthesia should therefore take Space, Time and Matter into account. It is possible that certain applications of the pendulum and rod which ignore these fundamental conditions may obtain results, but they are outside the domain of true Radiesthesia. This question will be examined in greater detail on page 65, and will form the subject of a special chapter. It will not be the first time that one and the same instrument has been employed for different ends.

Radiesthesia can also be defined in terms of one of the purposes for which it is used, such as an auxiliary to various sciences—Geology, Agriculture, Nutrition, Medicine, etc., or as a method based on the use of the perception of external influences obtained by movements of the hands held in the appropriate manner.

The remarkable thing about Radiesthesia is its wide field of application. It appears less a separate science than a technique of manifold applications, always playing an ancillary part with respect to the science to the help of which it has been summoned.

The dowser's instruments regarded as an extension of the sense of Touch ("Le Toucher, roi des Sens les surpasse en Richesse", wrote the poet Delille) can be compared with the microscope in relation to the sense of Sight; it serves as an amplifier of many uses, but, like the pendulum, requires suitable arrangement, focusing and minute adjustment.

Like many other sciences and technical arts, Radiesthesia has undergone a long period of incubation from which it now appears to be emerging. Let us hope that it will not be long before it fills the wide sphere of usefulness which many foresee.

Finally, Radiesthesia must not be expected to function outside the laws of Sensation, nor yet in doubtful cases; any application not amenable to the methods of check which I have described should be classified as Teleradiesthesia.

CHAPTER III

GENERAL TECHNIQUE

MANY methods have been described during the last few years, but when examined closely they are seen all to be based on the four methods of Fields, Samples, Series and Colours. The two first are old and the two latter modern. I will confine myself to these four methods, which are common to all radiesthetists, as a foundation for the instruction of beginners. Afterwards anyone will be able to supplement his technique from his own experiences or by reading the books of our best exponents. And so, leaving aside personal predilection, I will try to present something in the nature of an ABC of Radiesthesia.

METHOD OF FIELDS

The method of Fields goes back to the seventeenth century, and is described in the works of the period quoted by me above. This method is indispensable and cannot be replaced by any other, and the same can be said of the method of Samples which dates from that century. The first objects of study should be those known to possess electric, magnetic or calorific properties, such as rubbed glass or ebonite, magnets, stoves, then a fissure in the ground water-bearing or otherwise, ore, plants, the human body, finally anything at all.

Every object is surrounded by a 'field'—that is to say, a space in which its influence is felt. Every field is characterised by its vertical and horizontal dimensions, as well as by its 'direction', as shown by a beam of radiation acting at an angle to the meridian which is peculiar to the object. This conception is not the exclusive property of Radiesthesia.

Adjust your pendulum over an object, then move the hand holding it to one side. When the pendulum has moved away from over the surface of the object, it begins to oscillate towards it. When the hand is moved slowly one notices a change in the movement of the pendulum after a few centimetres, denoting the limit of the primary and horizontal field (or zone) peculiar to the object. Similarly, there appears a secondary and more extensive field both in the horizontal and vertical directions, ending, like the primary, with a gyration of the pendulum. Beyond these limits, which are always quite small, nothing more is discernible. To find the *direction* of a field, called by many dowsers the Fundamental Ray, move round the object with the pendulum oscillating within the limits of its field. At a certain point the pendulum will gyrate, giving the 'direction' of the ray.

Again, if the object can be held in the hand, pivot slowly on yourself with the pendulum gyrating over the object. At a certain point the pendulum will start to oscillate in the 'direction' of the field.

In my case the principal directions are: gold—west; lead—north-west; mercury—north; copper—north-east; silver—east; tin—south-east; iron—south; zinc—south-west.

The primary horizontal fields of the above metals extend from 20 cm. for lead to 70 cm. for iron. The primary field of an object rarely exceeds one metre; this appears to be constant regardless of the size of the object. The secondary field extends from a little more than a metre for a small object to several metres for an elongated object or one buried deep in the ground.

For springs of water, trees, narrow streams, etc., this

field bears a close relationship to their depth, height or length. Greater apparent distances, sometimes perceptible, are outside the sphere of Radiesthesia proper and are not proof against the checks we have described. The height of the vertical field of an object provides the first method for estimating mass and quantity. Another method consists in making the pendulum oscillate and in counting the oscillations until the pendulum begins to gyrate again. The number of oscillations provides a coefficient. It is as well to swing the pendulum rather forcibly.

Say you are standing within either the horizontal or vertical field of an object, on the same level with it or above it. In the first case, point at the object with the first finger of the left hand; the pendulum adjusted will gyrate.

Turn to the right and walk along a line perpendicular to that you were facing. After several paces the pendulum which was oscillating will gyrate; the distance thus traversed should be equal to that which separated you from the object. If it is otherwise an explanation must be found. To find depth, do likewise, but by moving away from your position vertically above the object. To correct mistakes of depth, measure a distance starting from a position above the object. Walk at right angles as before and see whether this new distance traversed is equal to or less than the first.

Methods of Check and Identification

I have already described several methods of check, but they will serve only to confirm that you have sensed something objective and external to yourself. They will not tell you the physical nature of the influence felt if this be not known beforehand. This is why, ever since 1930, when I began to publish my journal, *La Chronique des Sourciers*, which ceased to appear in 1940, I have wished that engineers with their laboratory instruments would verify the statements of dowsers and try to find out instrumentally to what the indications of Radiesthesia, especially those on the ground, may correspond.

Work of this sort has been done in France by M. Cody, but it is Mr. Maby in England who has done the most in this direction. The question is of primary importance, for on it depends the answer to the question whether Radiesthesia is pure and simple divination or, on the contrary, the registration by our hands of physical phenomena. This should be the first question to be settled in discussions between dowsers and scientists.

The dowser states that at a certain point on the ground or on the human body he obtained a reaction with his rod or pendulum. The first thing to be done should be to verify by means of a laboratory instrument whether this reaction corresponds to any known physical cause acting at the point indicated. If such verification could be made consistently, the cause would be accepted. This was realised by Mr. J. C. Maby who has published the results of his experiments in the important work called *The Physics of the Divining Rod* (G. Bell & Sons), written in conjunction with Mr. T. Bedford Franklin.

Studying the results of the method of Fields, at first on metal conductors and then on the reaction bands found by dowsers on the ground, he ascertained that these reactions, examined with electrometers, magnetometers, milli-ampère meters and ionisation counters corresponded to corpuscular and wave effects. There is then an agreement between the claims of the dowser and the statements of the physicist. The latter, however, can give a name to what the former has found and can point to the physical cause of the reactions.   It is much to be desired that such methods of verification should not be limited to occasional experiments in a laboratory, but should, on the contrary, be the normal practice when prospections are made.

I have already remarked that the movements of the rod and pendulum were subject to the laws of the Sensations, including Relativity.   In other words, the dowser may be deceived.   His art does indeed provide him with means of control, but how much more certain and convincing are those obtained from laboratory instruments, especially in the eyes of observers.   If the dowser could be accompanied in his prospections by an engineer, it would be of great advantage to him.   And the advantage would be mutual, for engineers, in their search for minerals and oil, have to carry about heavy and costly geophysical apparatus which must be set up at certain selected spots.   The dowser would indicate the best places according to his reactions, and there would thus be a great saving of time and money. Such procedure might be compared to the cooperation of a blind man and a paralytic!

ELECTRICAL RADIESTHESIA

We have just seen that the work of the pendulum and the rod can be compared with that of laboratory instruments.   If you were to examine such apparatus as motors, batteries, accumulators and so on with the rod or pendulum you would make some interesting discoveries, many being of practical value, such as the ability to find out whether an accumulator is charged or not, whether a current is passing in a wire and so on.   Other observations can be made by methods described later.   Experiments on electrical instruments have the further advantage of being capable of immediate check.   However, they have not hitherto been sufficiently numerous and thorough to deserve a chapter to themselves, so I have confined myself to pointing out in these few lines their possibility and their undoubted interest.

Use of the Rod

All the experiments mentioned can be carried out as well with the rod as with the pendulum. What I have already said on the subject of the rod should suffice to show how this instrument can be employed in the circumstances described instead of the pendulum. The gyration of the latter is merely replaced by the rising or dipping of the rod. It is generally found that the rod goes down over positive and rises over negative electricity, just as the pendulum gyrates clockwise in the first case and counter-clockwise in the second (except for people who hold the pendulum in the left hand and get reversed reactions). On this point it may be said that it is not a bad thing to practise working with either hand.

METHOD OF SAMPLES

The method of Samples was described in a very detailed manner in the works of the seventeenth century. It was the method used by the Baron de Beausoleil. In our own time it has been considerably improved on by Abbé Bouly, who reinforced it with the method of the Solar Plane, an offspring of the Meridian (or North-South) Plane. The method of samples is based on the following experiment :

Place on the ground or on a table two objects, alike or different, at a smaller distance from one another than the combined extent of their horizontal fields. If the objects are alike, you will observe that the pendulum adjusted over the first object continues to gyrate over the whole space which separates it from the second object and even over the whole surface of the latter.* It can then be said that harmony or accord exists between the two objects and the first is said to be a 'sample' (*témoin*) of the second.

If the objects are not alike nothing of the sort takes place, the pendulum gyrates only over the first object.

You can strengthen this accord by putting the two objects in line with the sun or with a magnet or by placing them on a meridian (N.-S. line).

You will also find harmony or affinity between the human body and a food that suits it. This is a special case which we will study (page 46) in discussing Alimentary Radiesthesia.

The Meridian and Solar Planes

You should begin by practising on a visible object which you have placed on the ground; it will be easy to pass on to objects, the position of which is unknown to you. Adjust the pendulum over a sample of the object held in the left hand and, starting at any convenient point, walk from east to west. In passing a certain point I, the pendulum will start gyrating if you are swinging it, or to oscillate if, whilst walking slowly, you have continued to let it gyrate over the sample. If you are using a rod you will get a reaction at this point. These reactions show that the object lies on the meridian through I. Go on walking in the same direction and you will get another reaction at A. If you have walked from west to east you will have got a reaction at A', after the indication at I. Go through the same procedure on another E.-W. line and you will obtain indications at the points I' and B, or if you walk from west to east, at B'. The lines BA and $B'A'$ meet

---

* For a long time I believed that a neutral place existed between the object and its sample, but later this idea did not appear to stand up to methods of check.

in the meridian through $I'I$ at O, where the hidden object should be found.

The point O can also be found by following a line parallel to II', when a reaction will occur at O'.

In the method of the Solar Plane, the N.-S. line is replaced by the line between the sun and the object. This is found in the same manner as described for the

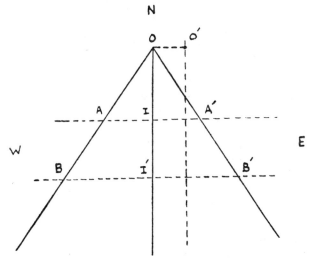

Fig. 6.   The Meridian and Solar Planes.

Meridian Plane, the reactions at I and I' occurring when you pass between the sun and the buried object.   To find other lines passing through the object you have only to go through the same procedure after the sun has changed its position.   In this way you can obtain several lines intersecting at the point where the object should be found.

This method is more accurate than that of the Meridian Plane.

If you are using a rod, hold the sample against one of its

branches and give it a quick sideways movement from left to right.   By rising or dipping, the rod will give the direction.

If you are prospecting for an object of large extent, such as a water-bearing fissure, narrow stream and so on, you can disregard the sun and the meridian, and 'explore the horizon' with your left arm extended—that is to say, make a slow circular movement with intent to find a line perpendicular, in this case, to that of the object, holding a sample or not according to the circumstances.

Then a strange thing happens.   The pendulum seems to be drawn towards the object, and all you have to do is to follow it.   As soon as you have reached the line of the object the pendulum will pass from oscillation to gyration, or will continue to follow the line.   If you make it deviate slightly it will return to the line.   Maybe that a trick of the hand is involved which is not acquired at the first attempt. These effects cannot be produced with the rod.   The sideways movement gives the indication of direction.   When you reach the line the rod will react; you must then draw back, then advance either to right or left.   You must work with abrupt movements, though with the pendulum the action is continuous.   I hope I have been clear in my description of this technique; it is easy to understand when actually witnessed, but is difficult to describe.

Means of Control

The method of Samples lends itself to exercises of control, some of which may assume a sporting character, and even form the basis of competitions.

For example, you can place two similar lumps of metal 2 metres apart, one serving as a sample of the other.   In order to strengthen their combined field (which is not really essential), you orientate them on a meridian or in line with the sun.   If you pass between the two lumps with a pendulum adjusted over a sample (you can use a hollow pendulum to hold the sample), you will find that your pendulum will gyrate. You work in a similar manner with the rod.

These experiments can be carried out with the eyes closed, and this is where the game comes in.

A variation of this exercise consists in walking backwards at the start. As you cannot see behind you, you can keep the eyes open, which makes this experiment less difficult than the preceding one.

If you are in the country, another variation consists in cutting the plane passing through a tree on a meridian or solar line, without a sample in the case of fruit-trees or trees like the lime or ash infusions from which are used medicinally (in such cases it is the human body which acts as a sample), or with a leaf as a sample for trees in general.

It is this last experiment, invented by me, using a rod, many years ago after a meeting with Abbé Bouly, which convinced me of the utility and interest of the dowser's art.

What I have just said about the rod and the 'closed eyes' and the stepping backwards shows that the method of Samples is effective in demonstrating the objectivity of the instrument's reactions.

However, the evidence for the effectiveness of samples and of the justification for their use should be completed by means of laboratory experiments, as has been done for the method of Fields.

The practical outcome would be a proof of the existence between two metallic masses of the same composition, of a field possessing definite physical characteristics.

I believe that Mr. Maby has carried out research to this end. This work, though not yet completed or published in detail, shows that the use of samples also rests on an objective physical basis. It is the more important in that there is a tendency for many people to attribute to the sample merely a 'psychic' value.

METHOD OF SERIES

The conception of a series of continuous movements of the rod or pendulum producible up to 'saturation', if one may say so, must be of a great antiquity, as the idea is a natural one, but I have not been able to find any positive reference to it before the writings of Abbé Mermet and the correspondence I had with him. Hence it is to him that I ascribe this method. It enjoys by no means the same popularity as the two methods already described, but, as it can be most useful on occasion, I have thought it well to mention it.

By SERIES is meant the numbers of the groups of gyrations obtained by the consecutive repetition of the movements of the pendulum over an object.

To find these groups, you must adjust the pendulum over the object; then draw back, and the pendulum will pass to oscillation. Start the oscillation again; the pendulum will again gyrate over the object; again draw back and start again—and so on—until the pendulum no longer has the strength, so to speak, to gyrate, and remains in a state of oscillation.

The sum of these groups of gyrations which you have elicited is called the 'Series' of the object over which you have worked. You should count the final oscillations, as their number will give a coefficient distinguishing one series from another when these series contain the same number of groups of gyrations.

It can be seen then that the Series, which is *a sum of groups of gyrations* obtained after adjustment, is further distinguished by the simple enumeration of the oscillations which occur at the end of the operation. This counting of oscillations is often used for quite other purposes than Series, which is qualificative in nature and not quantitative.

Instead of alternately withdrawing and advancing with the pendulum, you can stop its movements by slight jerks of the hand, and so stay fixed throughout the operation.

The numbers in Series give the key to the nature of simple bodies and of a good many compound bodies, and taking the Series often enables an initial mistake in the

Some Useful Series

Clockwise:—

High frequency and radio-activity	. . . 15	Lead	. . .	11 or 13
Electricity and Magnetism	. 10	Tin .	. . .	8
Copper . , . .	5	Silver	. . .	7
Aluminium . . .	3	Zinc	. . .	6
		Iron	. . .	4
		Water	. . .	2

Counter-clockwise:—

Salt	3	Silica	. . .	5
Clay	7	Lime	. . .	3

direction of gyration, which has occurred inadvertently or for some other reason, to be rectified. For example, you have obtained an initial clockwise gyration over an object which is a bad conductor of electricity, but whilst taking the Series the gyration will become counter-clockwise of its own accord.

There is no difficulty in taking Series with the rod, but in that case the advance and withdrawal are essential.

The counting in Series begins after the first movement whether the instrument used is a rod or a pendulum. Remember that in working with the rod it is a good thing to move the hands rapidly to and from one another. Some radiesthetists say that there is a point of maximum instability for the two hands analogous to the point of adjustment in the pendulum, and this position is the one to be aimed at. One should not release one of the branches during the operation, though this practice is much to be recommended otherwise for dowsing in general.

One can observe a curious correspondence between the Series of simple bodies and their atomic weights.

METHOD OF COLOURS

All the methods I have described can easily be adopted by dowsers in general, but this does not seem to be the case with Colours. This method is recent, and owes its origin to M. Henri Mager. It has enjoyed a period of great popularity, which would no doubt persist, if only the disagreement between various operators could be removed or diminished.

Besides the work of M. Mager on this subject, the very interesting observations by Captain W. H. Trinder in his book *Dowsing* must be mentioned.

Colours are in the nature of 'samples', and can sometimes take their place. As Captain Trinder has truly remarked, they are less accurate than real samples, but are useful when general rather than special indications are required. Besides, colour samples take up little room, and are light to carry—an important point when prospecting. Some doctors have obtained very encouraging results by their use.

Most dowsers who use colours appear to find an accord between some particular colour and their own person and also an accord between the points of the compass and various colours.

In all respects colours seem to be individualistic; for instance, M. Mager and Captain Trinder find that North corresponds to violet and South to red, whilst other dowsers find the exact opposite.

I would advise every dowser to make a preliminary experiment to determine what in his case is the appropriate orientation of the colours and his own harmonising colour.

The operation is simple; you adjust your pendulum with counter-clockwise gyration over a colour and see whether it is in harmony with yourself—that is to say, whether there is a field of union between that colour and your left hand. For this purpose, take as your colours those of the rainbow —violet, indigo, blue, green, yellow, orange, red. For myself I am in harmony with blue-indigo.

If I now assume this colour in the shape of coloured ribbon or cardboard over which, held in the left hand, I adjust my pendulum, I will find the North-East when I pivot round, the pendulum at this point passing to oscillation. It is probable that those who find colour and direction differing from mine will in general obtain different results.

However that may be, the following are the colours and directions which in my case correspond with the metals stated:

Mercury	.	.	.	.	North; red
Copper .	.	.	.	.	North-east; blue-indigo
Silver	.	.	.	.	East; yellow
Tin	.	.	.	.	South-east; orange
Iron	.	.	.	.	South; violet
Zinc	.	.	.	.	South-west; grey
Gold	.	.	.	.	West; green
Lead	.	.	.	.	North-west; sky-blue

Colour 'Series' are taken on ribbons or bits of coloured cardboard, the pendulum gyrating counter-clockwise with the thread at 6 cm. for violet, 16 for red, 20 for white.

The numbers in the Series are as follows:—

White	.	.	.	. 15	Sky-blue	.	.	.	. 8
Red	.	.	.	. 12	Indigo-blue	.	.	. 7
Orange	.	.	. 11	Violet	.	.	.	. 6
Yellow	.	.	. 10	Grey	.	.	.	. 3
Green	.	.	.	. 9	Black gives no Series			

You of course verify your Series and Colours by means of our four methods of check.

CHAPTER IV

DOWSING FOR WATER

IF it were only a question of digging an occasional shallow well, a profound knowledge of geology could be dispensed with, but the case is not the same if you intend to offer your services to neighbours, public or private bodies, towns or villages.

In such cases you must bring to bear all your resources and a knowledge of geology is one of the most important. It is not because geology can often tell you where water is to be found, but because it tells you where there is barely a hope of finding it, thereby sparing you many painful mistakes.

Moreover, in the course of your prospections for water, you are likely to meet hydraulic engineers and professional geologists, and you ought to be able to understand what they are saying, talk the same language and read their maps, which will sometimes be of the greatest help. Besides, Geology is not a difficult subject to learn. In France it is a part of the fourth-class curriculum which is followed by children of twelve years. Elementary class-books have been written for their benefit, which are unnecessarily complete for children and quite adequate for teaching the essentials.

In England, too, there are excellent elementary manuals which you would do well to study—for instance, *An Introduction to Geology*, by A. E. Trueman, Murby, 1938, 4*s.*, and *Teach Yourself Geology*, by A. Raistrick, Eng. U.P., 1944, 3*s.*

Wells and Springs

Apart from the necessity for geological knowledge, the discovery of water by dowsing is not a difficult or complicated affair. However, to make the start more easy, I advise you to begin by observations on wells and springs. You will then start from something of which you already have the answer, and you will be in a better position to make your early efforts successful, the more so since you will be able to check some of your results. On the other hand, I cannot recommend too strongly that, later on, when you have to carry out serious work involving considerable expense, if the country is new to you, always to begin your prospections with a careful study of the wells and springs in that area, for you will get really valuable information thereby.

LOCATING A STREAM

When the water in a well or spring is not due to an underground sheet (*nappe d'eau*), which is usually the case, it is supplied by a stream (*courant d'alimentation*), which often comes from a great distance. Frequently, especially in the case of springs, the appearance of the soil will be a guide to the direction.

Begin by adjusting your pendulum. Personally, I use methods of adjustment which are perhaps somewhat empirical, but which have nevertheless always given me good results. The first consists in adjusting the pendulum over the left hand at about 13 centimetres. This adjustment will give you the two lines which bound the stream (R and R' in Figure 7), the first found by approaching, the second either by advancing slowly or by crossing over to the other side and returning over the same ground. These two lines are often only a few centimetres apart.

This adjustment is effected through the water contained in the human body acting as a sample. The second adjustment is made on the ends of the fingers of the left hand, palm held upwards. It occurs at about 4 centimetres and may be connected with high frequency and radioactivity. This short adjustment will mark the medial line of the stream and will serve as a sort of check on the next operation.

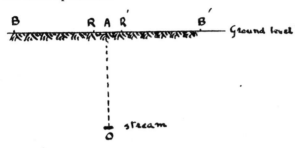

FIG. 7. An Underground Stream without Complications.

The depth $AO = AB$ or AB'. R and R' are the apparent edges.

If there is a layer of clay between the surface and the stream, AB and AB' are noticeably smaller than AO.

Now move round the well or spring. As soon as you find what you take to be a line of reaction, draw back a little and begin the operation again, advancing to one side; the pendulum will meet the line again and gyrate. Continuing in this way you will obtain a series of points which will enable you to peg out a line of the required length.

Instead of the procedure of withdrawing and advancing again to one side, you can follow the line as described on page 22. You look for the second line as explained above.

Yield

It is good practice in modern prospection to begin with

the yield, for if it is insufficient one can search elsewhere without wasting time in finding the depth.

Many of our fellow-dowsers aim at giving a very precise estimate. I do not consider myself capable of doing this, and confine myself to estimates of a general kind such as, weak, moderate, good. I have always considered that very precise figures savour of divination. On the other hand, exact estimates can always be obtained by pumping or in other familiar ways.

You have four methods at your disposal for estimating the yield of a well:

(1) The first method consists in adjusting the pendulum over the stream and then counting the number of oscillations. In my case this rarely exceeds twenty for a very strong flow.

(2) Lay a magnet or compass over the line of the stream. Adjust the pendulum as above, then move round the compass. The number of revolutions made by you before the normal gyrations again occur at the four cardinal points will give an indication of the yield.

(3) With your pendulum gyrating over the stream, hold your left hand motionless at the level of your right hand and slowly raise the latter with the pendulum still gyrating. When it passes to oscillation you will have raised your hand through a certain height which bears a relation to the yield.

(4) In following the stream you will come across lines of reaction at right angles to it which can be followed. Their length is proportional to the yield.

Depth

As in the case of yield, it is a good thing to begin with a well which can be measured, and will therefore serve as a basis for comparison.

You have at your disposition the following methods, which are capable of being checked:

(1) Draw up a scale corresponding to the height of your body (or to a 2-metre rule held upright), in which zero is at the level of the eyes and 50 metres * at the level of the waist. Lower the little stick of the adjusted and oscillating pendulum from the level of the forehead. The pendulum, by changing its movement, will indicate the depth in metres.

(2) Count aloud in metres at a rate arrived at by previous experiments over existing wells until the pendulum moves.

(3) Reckon the distance whilst walking over the ground from the middle of the stream and at right angles to its course, until you get a gyration of the pendulum. This point is on the 'line of depth' or 'depth parallel'. (See B and B', in Fig. 7.) This is the best method and should always be used.

These methods can be checked in two ways:

(a) By carrying a bar magnet or a compass over which you hold your pendulum at about 6 centimetres and walking as already described. After a certain number of paces the pendulum will change its movement, giving you a depth often much greater than that obtained without the magnet.

(b) Move away from the stream for a measured distance, say 6 metres. Point at the stream with your left hand stretched out as an antenna. Adjust the pendulum. Make a right turn and move off in the new direction at right angles to the first. If you get a gyration at 6 metres, no correction is necessary; but if you get it at only 3 metres, you must double your coefficient for depth.

---

* The corresponding measurement is peculiar to each dowser. English dowsers would naturally make the unit a foot.

Most dowsers find that a layer of clay falsifies calculations for depth and have to increase the figure obtained by the usual methods.

Potability

You examine the stream in exactly the same way as a piece of food, as explained in Chapter VI.

STREAMS AND FISSURES

Having practised the experiments over wells and springs which I have described, you can now start on Prospection properly so called.

Adjust your pendulum and make a survey of the horizon with your left arm extended as a movable antenna, if we may so express it.

At a certain point your pendulum will gyrate, and you must then walk in that direction. When you have reached the line of the stream, your pendulum, which was oscillating, will gyrate. It then remains for you to mark out the water-bearing fissure, and examine its yield, depth and potability as described above.

However, a difficulty may arise through the insignificant streams often met with in certain soils. You should then use the supplementary methods already referred to as the third and fourth methods of check (cf. p. 8)—namely, the 'point' and the 'deep breath', thereby eliminating the effect of smaller streams.

For a good site for a well, choose the intersection of two streams which you have traced and pegged out. You will get a better yield at such a spot.

It may happen that you are examining an area where there are shallow streams liable to pollution. Water must then be sought at greater depths. Certain formations contain several layers of water. These are encountered one after the other as the pendulum is lowered vertically. When the desired level is reached the streams at that level can be sought, using the left hand as an antenna as described above. You will in this way pick up a different set of streams, which are more likely to be potable than those nearer the surface.

The search for streams and water-bearing fissures always takes much time and care, especially for a dowser who, like myself, cannot sense the stream until reaching the line of depth; moreover, in certain soils streams are at a considerable distance from their concomitant and parallel depth lines. In such cases geological knowledge is of value for indicating in which quarter you should search.

In spite of accurate adjustment it may happen that a reaction of the pendulum may be due to some other cause than water—for example, a dry fissure. Take the Series of what you have found. If it is water the Series will be two followed by seven oscillations. If it is electricity or magnetism the Series will be ten.

Note also that when there is a stream of water the pendulum follows it easily when you walk down-stream in the middle, but has a tendency to gyrate when you are moving up-stream. Here you have a method of estimating the strength and velocity of the stream. If, on the contrary, you are following a dry fissure the pendulum will behave in the same manner in both directions.

Hot and Mineral Springs—Automatic Adjustment of the Pendulum

It may happen that you want to locate hot or mineral springs—that is to say, something out of the common. In such cases your usual adjustment would clearly be of no effect; you must provide yourself with a sample of a special kind—namely, that of the water you are seeking. The best procedure is to use as a pendulum the little vessel with a string handle to which the thread, wound on the little stick, is fastened (see p. 5). Put some cotton-wool in the vessel. It will prevent the water used as a sample from splashing out.

You are no longer adjusting your pendulum on an object below it, but on the actual water it contains. This operation is performed with no more difficulty than the ordinary adjustments, and is equally efficacious. You work clockwise, as mineral water is a good conductor of electricity.

It often happens that certain kinds of water require a greater correction for depth than ordinary water. You will notice this if you fill a glass of some special water and place it at the foot of a table; adjust a pendulum over the water at the level of the table, and then move it to one side. Instead of changing its movement at a distance equal to the height of the table, it may do so at a distance equal to only a quarter of the height. The depth found in prospection would then have to be multiplied by four.

Ascending Waters

These are springs which, acting on the principle of pressure tanks, rise to the surface by vertical channels. They are revealed on the ground by patches of negative electricity. To recognise these patches, adjust the pendulum for negative electricity—for example on a bit of ebonite which has been rubbed with wool. Such spots are often suitable for the digging of wells. We will come to this again in discussing Agricultural Radiesthesia.

THE ROD AND MR. MABY'S EXPERIMENTS

In dowsing for water some people prefer the rod because it is not affected by the wind. Others remain faithful to the pendulum, a rather heavy one for choice, say 60 to 80 grammes (about 2 to 2¾ oz), because it leaves the hand free, a great advantage when the prospection is long and the ground very up and down. Moreover, the pendulum admits of a stream being easily followed, whilst the rod demands an endless succession of forward and backward movements, which is rather tiring.

Mr. Maby, whom I have already mentioned (p. 17), recommends the holding of the rod with the point towards the body. The curious thing is that when long ago I started dowsing I did hold the rod in this manner, but then gave it up rather with the idea of doing as others did. Fundamentally, Mr. Maby is right. His hold with the hands palms downwards is more normal, and the grip with the hands makes it easy to keep the rod horizontal, so that the rise and dip of the rod are clear cut.

Mr. Maby has, with his laboratory instruments, fully confirmed the influences felt by the dowser in the open; the two edges of the fissure, the line of depth, the transversal lines which are of magnetic origin. On both sides of the stream he observes a series of positive and negative parallels. The dowser who habitually walks too quickly rarely notices these parallels. A very interesting observation of Mr. Maby is that the whole positive and negative system is liable to change—in other words, at one time all the parallels will be negative and at another time positive.

It is greatly to be desired that whenever a dowser undertakes important work of prospection involving considerable further expense, he should be accompanied by an engineer provided with instruments. If this were done, the dowser would be taken more seriously by the scientific world as well as by his clients. In the same category as this confirmation by means of electrometers and other apparatus, may be quoted a photographic method which has often been tried with success. For three or four days a packet containing a photographic plate protected by lead sheet pierced with holes is left over a stream. When the plate is developed, the holes in the lead sheet will be clearly marked. The same thing will not occur if a plate similarly prepared is placed to one side of the stream. A variation of this procedure carried out by M. Cody consists in leaving some activated charcoal at a point over the stream, and then bringing it to an electroscope. The use of sulphide of zinc has also been recommended, as it will be seen to sparkle when examined under the microscope.

CHAPTER V

DOWSING FOR MINERALS AND METALS

IF a knowledge of Geology is necessary for prospecting for water, it is even more so for the prospection of minerals. In practice it is only mining engineers and technicians who are interested in Radiesthesia of minerals, the which, by the way, is capable of being of the greatest service to them. They alone possess the necessary knowledge and, I may add, the opportunity, for the radiesthetic prospection of a mining concession demands long and minute research if a satisfactory result is to be obtained; needless to say, that such research should be undertaken in conjunction with the use of geophysical methods.

I will, however, make one exception. If you live in a country rich in minerals, it would be very interesting for you, apart from prospection of any kind, to make a collection of stones and minerals. It is a very pleasant job for an amateur, and is a good excuse for numerous excursions, and may even be the cause of really useful contribution to science. If then you inhabit one of those favoured districts you would do well to study Radiesthesia of minerals. You will, however, need a technical book as a guide, such as Frank Rutley's excellent *Elements of Mineralogy* (Murby, London).

IDENTIFICATION OF SPECIMENS

The pendulum can be adjusted over any piece of ore in the manner already explained. It will gyrate clockwise over all minerals and metals which are good conductors of electricity and counter-clockwise over others.

The hollow pendulum, charged with a 'sample', and adjusted over the specimen, will oscillate after being raised slowly through several centimetres, if there is accord between the sample and the specimen; otherwise it will continue to gyrate.

In a composite body one can distinguish metals from non-metals; thus in lead sulphide the sulphur and the lead can be distinguished separately by means of samples.

In the process of adjusting the pendulum, starting with the thread completely rolled up, different points of suspension will be found for the metal and the non-metal. The use of Series will give a rough analysis. If, on the other hand, the adjustment is made by rolling up the thread on the little stick, it appears to apply to the specimen as a whole.

ANALYSING A SPECIMEN

You want to know whether a specimen of quartz, for example, contains gold. Lay your specimen on the table after making certain that there is no subterranean stream beneath it, as this would spoil your experiment. Then place a sample of gold a few centimetres from the quartz. Adjust your pendulum over the gold, and see whether it gyrates between the gold and the specimen. If it does, the latter contains gold.

You can strengthen the field between the gold and the stone either by placing them on a meridian or in line with the sun or else in the extension of the length of a bar magnet and close to it. The degree of this extra strength can be measured by counting the oscillations over the field after adjustment, and before and after the methods I have just indicated. The content of a metal in any specimen can be found by using the methods described for finding the yield of a stream of water (page 31). Here again you will be wise to employ adjectives and not figures.

If you require greater precision you can use the method recommended by Abbé Bouly, which may be summed up thus: Place a little way apart your specimen of mineral and a little heap of the powder of the metal it contains; the pendulum, when adjusted, gyrates between the two. Get an assistant to remove progressively small quantities of the powder. After a time the pendulum will change to oscillation, although there may be some powder left. This residue will indicate the quantity of metal in the specimen, somewhat on the principle of a balance.

What I have just stated shows that the analysis of a specimen can be carried out very rapidly. When you make an excursion after minerals, you should take a set of samples with you and complete it by taking the 'series' and 'colours' of the metals and minerals you are likely to find; you will not be overburdened. The methods I have just described will enable you to make a selection on the spot from the specimens you pick up. You will then have much less to carry home in the evening before making a conclusive analysis by chemical methods or with the blow pipe.

PROSPECTION FOR VEINS AND MASSES

Ores are found in the form either of veins or masses. The former are elongated deposits which can be detected somewhat in the manner of water-bearing fissures, for the deposits are mostly fissures filled with ore. Masses, on the other hand, are more or less considerable accretions, fairly compact and quite separate. Books on Geology will tell you how ores are distributed in various areas.

Load your hollow pendulum, of wood or earthenware, and adjust it automatically (page 36). Explore the surroundings with your left hand extended as an antenna. You can get results with certainty only at short distances— those not greater than the depths, but distances are increased on a solar or meridian line.

Like many of my fellow-dowsers, I used to think that it was possible to sense the objective at very long distances. One day I was making an excursion in a mining area accompanied by an engineer. Having explored the horizon with my pendulum containing the sample, I indicated several distant spots in various directions. My engineer was astounded, as he knew there were mines in those directions at a distance of many kilometres. Being suspicious of such easy success, I walked forward in one of the directions indicated. After a few steps I stopped at a line revealed to me by series and other methods of check as that of an underground stream. The same thing occurred at spots in other directions. This shows, firstly, that one should hesitate before making a positive statement, and secondly, that in spite of the sample the physical effects caused by water-bearing fissures dominate all others, and so may lead you into error.

However, let us suppose that you are actually in the presence of a vein or a mass. Walk along it until gyration of the pendulum indicates that you have reached the edge. You will find as you walk along that the swinging pendulum seems to choose the best directions of itself, you only have to 'follow' it, so to speak. Having reached the edge of the vein or mass, the pendulum will either gyrate if you stand still, or follow the edges of the vein or mass (cf. p. 22). Now peg out the line you have followed.

Instead of a hollow pendulum you can use an ordinary pendulum carried over a small narrow strip of wood held in the left hand on which are fastened two similar samples 15 cm. or so apart. The pendulum adjusted in the field between the two samples, will take the direction of the first vein it comes across. This method was invented by Abbé Ferran.

You can use a rod with a sample held in the right hand and squeezed against the rod.

For estimates of quantity ('yield' in the case of water), depth and so on, you proceed exactly as for water, notably for mineral waters (page 36).

CAVITIES, VALUABLES, COAL AND OIL

Cavities and cellars can be found with a pendulum, hollow or otherwise, adjusted at 19 cm. For the rest, you work as on a water-bearing fissure. Dry cavities and fissures will not give any series, or, perhaps I should say, the series of 'one', or else alternate movements of gyration and oscillation.

The search for valuables is very disappointing. If they are in a closed box forming a screen you will not be able to sense them. If they are loose, it may well be that the quantity is too small to make an impression. I must admit, however, that my son and myself have succeeded in discovering most of the hiding-places in which certain people during the two wars had buried valuables of various kinds, silver, gold and jewels, etc. These objects presented a considerable bulk and were not buried deep, and their containers, generally of wood, had burst open or had rotted through damp. It was a question of finding a burial-spot which the owners could not remember exactly, though they were able to give a general idea of the position. The method used was that of the Solar Plane, supplemented by that of the Meridian Plane, and the objects were found at the intersection of the two planes. As I have said above, this method admits of work being done at distances of some 50 m. measured from a probable centre, and this seems a wide enough margin for this kind of prospection.

A frequent source of error is due to small masses of radioactive soils. They respond to samples of metals of many kinds. You may get a reaction for gold and be full of hope. You try silver, and your hope is confirmed. Then you try nickel, which formerly was not used for coins; your pendulum will gyrate the more violently, but your hope dies out. However, you may have found a deposit of radioactive soil which is not to be despised.

In estimating the depth of coal and oil, a coefficient must be used as in the case of mineral waters. Liquid oil can easily be confused with gas. My serial number for oil is plus 6 followed by 24 oscillations, and for gas minus 6 followed by 14 oscillations.

CHAPTER VI

ALIMENTARY RADIESTHESIA

THE various applications of Radiesthesia described above require a certain amount of scientific knowledge and are intended for specialised types of dowser. 'Alimentary' Radiesthesia, on the contrary, has a very general appeal, and can be of service to everyone in their daily life. It requires little special knowledge; its methods are of the simplest, and can be followed by anyone, even by children.

When, after the war of 1914, my interest in Radiesthesia started, this branch of the subject had been barely thought of. One only knew that clockwise gyration of a pendulum, when adjusted over the hand above a piece of food, signified that it was good for one, whilst if the gyration were counter-clockwise the food was unsuitable. I think I was responsible for perfecting this primitive method by suggesting coefficients and measurements.

I mentioned this application of Radiesthesia in the first edition of *Le Sourcier Moderne* in 1929, and I may say that I had met with few failures. But except from the American physician, the regretted Dr. Selige of Miami, I received little encouragement. He fully understood the importance of the subject, and expressed the opinion that instruction in it should be widespread and begin in schools. He founded several societies which since his death have been dissolved.

I will now describe the methods, all of a very simple kind, which are employed in this branch of Radiesthesia.

You have food of some kind on your plate. I assume it is good for you; anyhow, at first don't make too many experiments with the unknown.

45

Adjust your pendulum over the food, then pass your left hand between it and the pendulum. You will then observe a curious and unexpected phenomenon: normally the pendulum would pass from gyration to oscillation owing to the screening of the hand; but now it continues to gyrate, which shows that there is accord or affinity between yourself and the food. If the pendulum gyrated in the opposite direction there would be discord, showing that the food would be definitely bad for you. But if the pendulum started to oscillate, this would not necessarily mean that the food was bad, it might mean merely that there was too much of it! Reduce the portion and try again, but instead of passing your hand between the dish and the pendulum, you need only stop the original gyration and observe in which direction the pendulum starts oscillating. If the food is good for you, the oscillation will take place towards your own body; otherwise it will deviate until the oscillation is parallel with the front of your body, which means that the food does not suit you.

Hitherto you have only obtained indications of a general kind, but now you are going to discover others which will give more precise and detailed information.

Your pendulum is gyrating over your left hand, which you have interposed between the food and the pendulum. Stop the gyration, make the pendulum oscillate, and count the oscillations. In practice they will not exceed 20. This procedure enables a system of coefficients to be adopted which is extremely useful. You can take it that at a figure of less than 10 the food is mediocre or, what is more usual, in too great quantity. With figures of 15 to 20 the food can be considered as very good.

You need not confine yourself to this method of co-efficients but can use another which consists in taking measurements along a horizontal rule, lying if possible in a meridian, starting from the food. This method has a more scientific aspect than the other. A ruler of 40 to 50 cm. is long enough.

You can still adjust the pendulum over the left hand at first, and then move it towards and above your plate. If the pendulum continues to gyrate, you proceed as before.

The question of quantity is a very important one in matters of food, and Radiesthesia is a good judge. Supposing the pendulum has gyrated favourably over a portion of food or beverage. As often as not this only tells you that the *kind* of food is suitable. The coefficients or measurement will complete the information, but all this might sometimes produce confusion.

Therefore, you should at first dowse over a very small quantity, which you should increase progressively. You will then find that your pendulum, which was gyrating vigorously, after two or three additions to the food or drink will start to oscillate, showing that the amount on your plate or in your glass is sufficient for the time being. It only remains for you to chew slowly and conscientiously what you are eating. Food well masticated and saturated in saliva will have a higher coefficient.

You take your coefficients or measurements for another person over the food, as you would for yourself.

Another method of finding out whether the food is suitable is by cutting the meridian or solar plane which passes through the food. In crossing the line there will be a lift of the rod—and here is a method of using the rod in connection with questions of food—or gyration of the pendulum. When working over another person, it suffices to pass between that person and the food, but in doing so take care that they are not on the same meridian or solar plane, for then your observations would apply to yourself and not to the other.

This short description contains the whole of the technique of Alimentary Radiesthesia. It can be easily seen that it is by no means complicated and could, in fact, be applied by any intelligent schoolboy. One may add that the purchase of pendulums and rods would not weigh heavily on the scholastic budget, especially as such apparatus can easily be made at home.

Choice of Food

Let us now review the results already obtained in these later years through Radiesthesia of Foods. I will begin by saying that indications are strictly personal and apply only to the time at which they are obtained. It may well happen that food which reacts as 'good' in the morning will be found to be only 'fair' in the evening.

However, from a large number of observations carried out on several different individuals, it is possible to draw certain general conclusions.

One knows of the long-standing dispute amongst authorities on hygiene, dividing them into the two camps of vegetarians and meat-eaters. The verdict of Radiesthesia seems to be decisive.

It gives the highest coefficients and highest measurements to cereals, fruits and vegetables. Next, 'highly placed', come milk, butter, eggs, and lastly meat. One can therefore dispense with food of animal origin, but one can make use of it provided it be of good quality and eaten in moderation; Radiesthesia shows great insistence in these respects.

Water is revealed as the first of beverages, provided again that it be of excellent quality. On the subject of water and other drinks, I should say that in working over them it is essential to take a large glass and fill it to the brim. It is as well to raise the hand holding the pendulum to a certain height above a glass which is not entirely filled. Taken in moderate quantities, wine, beer and cider receive high coefficients. I must repeat that though these conclusions hold good for me they may not do so for others.

Cooking

The pendulum can be used for other purposes in this domain of study. It can be used not only to examine the food itself, but also the manner of cooking. Thus, vegetables stewed together without water—the more watery below others less watery—give much higher coefficients than vegetables simply cooked in water separately. This method of cooking vegetables over a slow fire is one of the best both from the point of view of palatability and of health, for it is far less destructive of vitamins than is boiling.

Finally, Radiesthesia furnishes an easy approximation to the solution of a problem of chemical analysis which can only be completely solved after a long, difficult and costly process, namely that of the content in calcium, iron, iodine, phosphorus, etc., of the different plants. All hygienists agree that there is an increasing lack in our constitution of certain mineral elements, which they name, but no one heeds them! Radiesthesia, when more generally known, will spread a knowledge of their work and draw attention to it. Nothing is easier for a dowser than to get hold of a few samples of limestone, phosphorus, etc., and to ascertain which vegetables contain them in appreciable quantity, and then arrange his meals accordingly. The mineral content of a plant is assimilable, but we cannot say the same of the same mineral obtained from a chemist's shop. Hence the possibility of treatment on dietetic lines—a much more pleasant process than treatment by drugs.

For a long time, even amongst intelligent people, there was a reluctance to take up Alimentary Radiesthesia, because it was thought to be entirely subjective and psychic. Experience showed me that it responded perfectly to all checks with the pendulum or the rod—the 'closed eyes' and any other. The rod is much less used than the pendulum in connection with foods. Practically it hardly has other application than the cutting of the meridian and solar planes; it could not be used for taking coefficients and measurements.

It is to be desired that engineers and doctors should with their laboratory instruments study the connections and affinities which may exist between the human body and various kinds of food. The question would then definitely emerge from the obscurity hitherto surrounding it, and therefrom the whole of humanity would derive the greatest benefit.

In closing this chapter I cannot too strongly recommend my readers to start their work with Alimentary Radiesthesia.

It provides a daily occupation performed easily and without fatigue, and really beneficial both to themselves and to their families. If they have to do their own cooking, they will find this daily task even more interesting, as well as more scientific.

It may not be too fanciful to hope that this application of Radiesthesia may eventually help to solve the grave problem of Human Alimentation, which is the source of all our past, present and future difficulties.

Regarded superficially it may appear of little account; in reality it is of the highest importance and worthy of the closest study.

CHAPTER VII

MEDICAL RADIESTHESIA

IF I have recommended that Radiesthesia of Minerals should be reserved for engineers, more strongly do I recommend that only qualified doctors should concern themselves with Medical Radiesthesia. Those who do me the honour of reading my book will see that it is not a complicated procedure, and they would be wrong in depriving themselves, through prejudice, of the great service which this method can render. They are often puzzled both in their diagnoses and in their choice of remedies. Why despise a method which can do no harm but may be of considerable assistance?

Diagnosis

The first mention of research in Medical Radiesthesia comes, I think, from the Comte de Tristan some time previous to 1870, as I have said on page 2. However, this branch of our art appears to have been taken up effectively after the war of 1914 by the Abbés Bouly and Mermet. In 1932 the lamented Dr. Martin received his Doctorate from the Faculty of Medicine of Paris on the strength of his thesis on 'Radiesthetic Diagnosis in Veterinary Medicine'. It was published with a note of thanks to the author for his useful advice. Its publication created a sensation in the medical world, and a large number of doctors have since become interested in our art.

Start with this fundamental fact: that the pendulum, adjusted over a healthy part of the body with or without the left hand held antenna-wise, will undergo a change of movement over an unhealthy area.

Advance or withdraw the pendulum so as to determine the depth of the organ or of the unhealthy area. Examine the vertebral column. A change of movement of the pendulum over a certain vertebra can give valuable information about the part of the body to which it corresponds.

When the pendulum has been adjusted over an unhealthy part, change it over to oscillation; the number of oscillations will be an indication of the seriousness of the disease.

You can also investigate by using powders of the respective organs or therapeutic products withdrawn from their tubes, as samples.

Human Products

It may happen that, for one reason or another, a doctor will be unwilling to operate on his patient. A specimen of urine, blood, saliva, etc., taken from the patient will enable him to make a diagnosis after returning to his home. Urine appears to give the best results. These human products, moreover, enable the effects of treatment to be followed at a distance.

Take a 2-metre rule graduated in centimetres and lay it North and South. The urine of a healthy person in a saucer at the end of the rule will cause reactions of the pendulum at 40 cm., and, if you like to go as far, 160 cm. A product from a sick person will give different and smaller readings. Certain dowsers have drawn up tables of measurements corresponding to various diseases. Not being a doctor, I have not been able to verify the correctness of these tables.

Others, using coloured screens, have observed that a screen of a certain colour interposed between the urine and the pendulum does not prevent gyration. This shows that accord exists between the urine and the colour, from which the nature of the disease can be deduced in accordance with a standard chart. Other doctors attach importance to the direction of the field. Obviously, any doctor can tabulate his results. Nevertheless, it would be interesting if a medical commission were to consider whether a unification of such tables could not be achieved.

It is worth while mentioning the investigation of the nervous tonus by Abbé Mermet. It is done over the fist reversed. Man in a normal state gives 10 oscillations, but many more if he is in a state of nervous depression. I believe that Abbé Mermet measured arterial tension between the thumb and first finger when widely separated.

The pendulum gyrates clockwise with a series of 6 followed by 30 oscillations over the hand of a man and of a woman.

Certain radiesthetists say that they can distinguish between male and female with the pendulum. I do not think they can do so without recourse to Superpendulism. Ordinary Radiesthesia can in any case produce good results in diagnosis and treatment. In my opinion it would be better to keep to solid ground than to court the uncertainties of unknown heights.

Remedies

Your pendulum has changed its movement over an affected area. An appropriate remedy placed on your left hand will bring back the original movement. I must repeat that whenever I mention a remedy or a drug of any sort, it must be in a free state, and not enclosed in a cachet, flask, etc., all such envelopes forming screens which prevent contact with the electric field of the atmosphere. Turn back to the chapter on Alimentary Radiesthesia; you will there find instructions not only for the prescribing of a regular diet, but also for finding suitable remedies; the procedure is the same in both cases, the coefficients and measurements being taken in exactly the same way. It may happen that a remedy indicated as good at one time may not be so at another. It may also happen that two remedies separately indicated as good may be shown as the reverse when tested together. Homeopathic remedies behave, from the radiesthetic point of view, exactly like others, in spite of their state of infinitesimal dilution. However, it seems impossible to determine their composition by means of samples, the minute quantity of some of their constituents being below the level of sensorial perception.

A good remedy placed at the end of the rule alongside the urine restores the measurements 40–160. You can therefore carry out at home, far away from the patient, a sort of diagnosis with the remedies you have at your disposal.

Injurious Rays

In 1932, at the time of the acceptance of Dr. Martin's thesis, Dr. Jules Regnault in France and Baron von Pohl in Germany drew attention to the question of *Rayons Nocifs*, for so were called the emanations issuing from the ground, usually from water-bearing fissures, and capable of aggravating numerous diseases, such as cancer, tuberculosis, nervous affections, rheumatism, etc.

Shortly after, the question was studied scientifically by M. Cody, who discovered by means of laboratory apparatus that these dangerous emanations were composed mainly of alpha particles. All this harmonised with the numerous observations which had previously been made by scientists on certain effects deriving from the soil and of physical origin.

This phenomenon appears to be accepted more or less everywhere to-day by the scientific world. M. Cody sent a report which attracted considerable attention to the International Congress of Biology at New York in 1939. Mr. Maby has devoted a number of pages to this subject in his book.

The wide interest taken in this question by radiesthetists in all countries has elicited much information which goes to confirm earlier experience. From 1934 I assisted in the first experiments of M. Cody at Le Havre by showing him how to use the pendulum. Scientifically, the existence of injurious rays can no longer be disputed, and it seems to be a matter of the first importance that doctors should know how to use the pendulum.

It is clear that if there is any suspicion of their existence, it should suffice simply to move the bed of the patient, but how can the evil be foreseen without the use of the rod or pendulum? Certainly the electroscope will detect the presence of these rays, but one must know exactly where to place it. Without the rod or pendulum there is no way of finding this out, the more so that these dangerous fissures are often only a few centimetres in width. One cannot therefore look to the electroscope for a general method of control. The rays possess great power of penetration and traverse the whole length of a building from foundations to attics.

Every serious doctor should therefore acquire a sufficient knowledge of Radiesthesia to know how to detect the position of a fissure in the ground. To neglect to do so is the more inexcusable if he can make an immediate check of the reality of the phenomenon with an electroscope or by means of a photographic plate free of leadfoil.

How can one protect oneself against injurious rays? Lead sheet, as used in Radiology, is effective, but only for a few days. After that it is saturated to the point of becoming dangerous to handle without the usual precautions which have to be taken in dealing with radioactive material. Various apparatus have been invented, but all I have seen up to now have appeared fanciful and of no value. In short, the best thing is to change the position of the bed. The same rule applies wherever the presence of these rays is found—offices, workshops, stables, cattlesheds, etc., for they are harmful to animals as well as to men.

CHAPTER VIII

AGRICULTURAL RADIESTHESIA

I DO not know whether the rod and pendulum were used in connection with agriculture prior to 1914, but immediately after, when there was a revival of dowsing, one often heard mention of its use for various agricultural purposes. I recorded several instances in an article I wrote in 1926 in the review *Les Etudes*, and later in the first edition of *Le Sourcier Moderne*.

Since then Agricultural Radiesthesia has been considerably developed, and a general picture of it can now be given.

Of all the branches of our art, Radiesthesia in its application to foods and to agriculture is destined to be the most popular. In the latter form it is of interest to millions of people, whether engaged in farming, gardening, the cultivation of wines or forestry.

The farmer, taking the word in its widest sense, is daily confronted by an infinity of embarrassing problems, most of which can be solved by Radiesthesia (we will give examples), and so we cannot advise him too strongly always to carry his pendulum in his pocket.

To begin with, he has to study the question of water supply; for water is essential to the farm, the garden and pasture-land. Often enough it is within his reach without his knowing it. By no means do I advise him to start looking for water at great depths, which would entail much expense and require a special knowledge of geology, but he can with advantage undertake the digging of wells up to 8 or 10 metres deep. The tapping of streams may be of great use in connection with stables and cowsheds. Numerous diseases of cattle can be avoided by a simple change of position or the shutting off of a corner of a stable which is penetrated by injurious rays.

Our farmer should also study Radiesthesia of foods, so that he may be in a position to examine the fodder he gives his animals from the two-fold point of view of quantity and quality. By so doing he will get better results and effect considerable economies.

Finally, he should have some knowledge of Medical Radiesthesia; perhaps not enough for the treatment of animals who are seriously ill, but sufficient to be able to realise the necessity for calling in the 'vet', who is often informed too late.

Apart from farmers of all kinds, Agricultural Radiesthesia can and should interest an immense number of young people, especially Boy Scouts, Girl Guides and those associated with Youth Movements. Children and young people should have no difficulty in manufacturing their own rods and pendulums. They soon learn to handle them—far more quickly than grown-ups. The competitive aspect of some of the control experiments cannot fail to appeal to them.

During walks in the country and in camp, Agricultural Radiesthesia can lend itself to an infinity of experiments, both attractive and instructive, connected not only with agriculture, but also with botany, natural history and geology. All these sciences become vastly more interesting when they can be studied in the light of experiments on the ground well away from the atmosphere of the classroom.

Application of the Method of Fields

Measure horizontally and vertically the field of an isolated lump of earth, of a piece of earth *in situ* (remembering that the pendulum gives measurements which apply only to an area of the size of the hand holding it), of a plant, a heap of seeds, a tree, an animal, etc. The larger the dimensions of the field, the more interesting is the object, from the point of view of vitality and vigour, whether it be vegetable or animal. Thus you can compare two lots of seed similar in appearance, two shrubs, two animals, and so on, and determine which is the better.

Before measuring the field, which is easily done with a 2-metre rule, you can start by counting the oscillations which occur after the initial gyrations when adjustment is carried out, thereby obtaining valuable coefficients (p. 24) which supplement the measurements.

You can take the measurements either in a vertical or in a horizontal direction; it is a matter of convenience. You can also take the directions of the fields either by moving round the object or by pivoting round holding the object in one hand and the pendulum adjusted over it in the other. These 'Directions' will give you much information. There are some vegetables, such as the potato, which it pays to plant in a N.-S. direction. M. Discry has remarked that there is a part of the potato which reacts strongly to the pendulum; if this part is placed towards the North, the yield is considerably increased.

Application of the Method of Samples

You have a lump of earth and some samples: lime, silica, potassium, etc. It is easy for you to make a rough analysis of your specimen of soil. Obviously, such an analysis cannot take the place of a chemical analysis in the laboratory, but it can be of some use. You can continue the radiesthetic analysis by the Balance method with powdered minerals (p. 41), which an assistant pours gradually into a heap near the specimen, whilst the pendulum is gyrating between the specimen and the powder.   When the amount in each is equal, the pendulum will pass to oscillation.

Manures

Take a hollow pendulum and fill it with lime.   Adjust it automatically (p. 36) over the soil.   As the latter usually contains a little lime, the pendulum will stop turning of itself at the end of several gyrations.   Now count the oscillations.   In this way you will generally get a somewhat high coefficient for the content of your soil in lime. It is very rare for a field to have a uniform distribution of lime, potassium, etc., over its whole extent.   Walk along with your pendulum swinging and 'following its lead' (p. 22).   The pendulum may indicate a surface content of 8, for example, but alongside, one of 12, and further on another of 9.   Suppose that a specimen of soil gives a content of 15, it will not be difficult for you to distribute your fertiliser in proportion to the requirements of the piece you wish to cultivate.   I do not think that any other method exists at present which allows of the fertiliser being applied so quickly and economically as that I have just described.   In default of such a method it is usual for a farmer to distribute manure at so much a hectare, and he is astonished when, as often as not, results fail to correspond either with his expectation or the expense.   The opposite would be the more surprising.   If the makers of fertilisers understood their own interests, they would be the first to advocate the use of the pendulum.

Samples can be very useful in the radiesthetic examination of foods for animals, as also in veterinary treatment by Radiesthesia.   For food and remedies the method for treating animals is much the same as that for human beings (cf. Chapters VI and VII).

Accords

In all countries and in all ages it has been observed that certain plants flourish in certain kinds of soil, and not in others. Soil can be improved by the addition of suitable fertilisers, but there must be a fundamental accord between the plant and the soil.

Now Radiesthesia can give you sure and swift information on this head. It is enough to adjust the pendulum over the plant, its seed or merely one of its leaves, to get an immediate answer.

You have only to present your pendulum, adjusted for the plant, over the soil. If it continues to gyrate in the same direction, you can be hopeful. If it gyrates in the opposite direction, you are confronted by a disharmony which it may not be possible to correct. If it merely oscillates, a certain amount of fertiliser will establish accord.

In discussing foods (p. 49) I have stated that certain vegetables contained lime, iron, iodine, etc., in appreciable quantities, which give them pronounced therapeutic and alimentary properties. These can be appreciated by the method of samples. Naturally, adjustment has to be followed by the taking of coefficients in order to get an idea of the approximate content.

As a matter of interest, I may mention that the hazel appears to contain gold, the lime silver, the beech copper, the oak iron, etc., but in infinitesimal quantities.

I have related, on page 23, that my first experiment in Radiesthesia was in connection with the Solar Plane, by walking between the sun and a tree with a leaf as sample. In this case *any* leaf of a tree of the same kind will suffice, but if you wish to obtain a reaction on the other side of the tree and in the same place, you must use a leaf from the tree itself. In the first case there is similarity, in the second identity, whence interesting conclusions from the biological point of view can be drawn.

Relying on this basic fact, M. Ravat has made experiments, by working on grape-stones and plants, which have led to the cultivation of hybrid vines of excellent quality. Others have done the same with apple-trees. In this order of ideas there seems to lie a method of selection which is well worth developing.

When examining the fruit-trees in an orchard, or the forest trees in a wood, you will notice that sickly, stunted and cancerous trees do not accord with the soil in which they are planted. Continuing your study, you will find that these trees are generally growing over a water-bearing fissure positively electrified, whilst the soil is usually negative. Therefore, when you are planting trees, avoid underground streams! You will also notice that all trees struck by lightning are standing over streams, especially those at the intersection of two streams (cf. p. 34).

I mention again that positive electricity, represented by rubbed glass, requires adjustment at about 10 cm. of thread, or when the arm is pointed upwards towards the positively charged atmosphere. Negative electricity, represented by rubbed ebonite or, more simply, the ground, always requires counter-clockwise adjustment at about 10 cm. of thread.

But if the zones positively charged are long and narrow in shape, there will be found on the ground more or less large patches negative in sign with a high coefficient, such as 12 or 15, whilst round about the coefficient may be the usual 5 or 6. It is in the middle of such patches that the best trees grow. This information is of value when you are planting. In the first case the radiation is harmful; in the second, beneficial. Bores carried out on such patches, especially when they are over streams, yield water under pressure (cf. p. 36) of excellent quality.

Since we are talking of trees and the care which should be taken in planting them, we may as well mention that the value of standing trees can be estimated by means of Radiesthesia. You adjust the pendulum with the hand held antenna-wise towards a tree, and the coefficient you get will give you an indication of its value as a trade commodity. Move round the tree with the pendulum in action. If the pendulum changes its movement, it will be a sign of a disease which is concealed by the bark.

To end this lengthy list of experiments, let us say that one must not forget the frequent application of our four methods of check. It will greatly increase your confidence.

Application of the Method of Series

'Series' has several useful applications in Agricultural Radiesthesia. I will mention a few which my readers will be able to supplement according to need.

Rain-water . . . -1	Clay . . . . -7
Lime . . . . -3	Magnesia . . . -9
Silica . . . . -5	Phosphorus . . . -10
Sulphur . . . -6	Kitchen salt . . . -13
Subterranean water $+$ or -2 according to atmospheric conditions		

As can be seen, most of these figures are negative, and are found with the pendulum gyrating counter-clockwise. The positive series of metals given on page 25, which can be useful on occasion, should be added to the list.

Application of the Method of Colours

Colours can be usefully and conveniently employed, as they do not entail extra weight when you are on the move.

Starting from the fact that my personal colour is indigo, I find the following accords:

Red	.	.	.	North; limestone
Yellow	.	.	.	East; clay
Violet	.	.	.	South; humus
Green	.	.	.	West; silica (sand)
Orange	.	.	.	South-east; vegetable mould

It is possible that other dowsers will find an entirely different set of harmonies.

Drainage

The drainage of certain lands is very often essential, but it is a costly operation. Radiesthesia admits of it being carried out in a more economical manner.

Adjust your pendulum either about 5 or about 13 cm. (see page 30), and hold it high up, the hand above the forehead. In this way you will sense the little shallow streams. Peg them out. Their small depth will enable them to be reached by digging, and so you will often be able to dig up your land completely, and that at small expense.

CHAPTER IX

TELERADIESTHESIA OR SUPERPENDULISM

M. HENRI MAGER has recorded that at the time of the 1913 Congress it was suggested to him that in the list of events there should be included an examination with the pendulum of maps, plans and photographs as an operation capable of producing veridical results. This proposal was considered so unusual, and even absurd, that it was not entertained. However, after the war of 1914 Abbé Mermet and several others followed it up, and were soon able to produce numerous results.

Abbé Mermet has collected his experiences in his book, *Comment J'Opère* (Paris, Maison de la Radiesthésie, 1935). Well before its appearance the match had been set to the train of powder, for since 1930 there had been a rage for this type of research, and to describe it the new word *Téléradiésthie* was invented. It soon ceased to be confined to radiesthetic examination of plans, and was extended to include the use of the pendulum to obtain replies to questions of all kinds. The pendulum alone was used, as the rod appeared unsuitable for this type of work.

Abbé Mermet was both a radiesthetist and a teleradiesthetist. This is to say he mingled the two processes, which was, I think, a mistake.

Joseph Treyve, whom I knew equally well, and who was a dowser no less remarkable, seemed to me to have adopted a method better suited to the ends in view and less encumbered with the old dowsing methods. I will describe it by giving a few examples which will reveal its complete originality.

His system consisted in putting a question capable of

being answered only by 'Yes' or 'No'. For 'Yes' the
pendulum gyrated clockwise, and for 'No' counter-
clockwise; oscillation signified 'No answer'. If he wanted
numbers, he counted the oscillations of the pendulum
occurring after a gyration until gyration began again.
There is no need to say that adjustment of the pendulum'
was not required, it sufficed to hold it at the most convenient length.

J. Treyve was a great hunter. On occasion he used the
map to find out the section of wood where wild boars were
harbouring. He moved his pendulum over the map or
round the edges so as to get lines of intersection, but if he
had no map he took a paper and pencil and drew one from
memory. It can therefore be seen that the various papers,
maps and so on play only an ancillary part, and that the
root of the matter lies in the question put and the answer
given through the medium of the instrument.

This will be more easily understood from the examples
of his work which I will give, but before doing so I think
it will be useful, for the benefit of those who want to experiment over a map or photo, to describe the simplest method
of procedure.

You hold your pendulum in the right hand and give it
a gentle swing. With the left hand you move a pencil over
the surface of the map or photo. When the point of the
pencil passes over a significant spot, the pendulum begins
to gyrate. You mark this point with the pencil. In this
way you can find a series of points, and, if desirable, draw
connecting lines. One can see that, compared with
ordinary Radiesthesia, the method of Teleradiesthesia or
Superpendulism is simple and rapid; it can be learnt in a
few minutes, but for successful practice requires a very
special aptitude.

Let us return now to M. Treyve.

One day he received a packet containing two stones with a request to find the spot, somewhere in France, where they had been picked up. After working a few minutes, he sent his inquirer the following answer, 'These stones were picked up three kilometres from Eysies in Dordogne', and he added, 'by a young, fair and pretty woman.' It was correct.

We can see how he set to work. Taking his pendulum, he put the following questions successively: 'Is it in the north, west, east, south, centre of France?' The pendulum gyrated for the centre. He then took a list of the Departments in the centre, and the pendulum gyrated only for Dordogne. He had an intuition, he told me, that the place might be Eysies, a locality much frequented by tourists interested in archaeology. The pendulum replied in the affirmative. He then asked whether it was at Eysies itself, or on the outskirts. Getting no answer for the place itself, he counted the oscillations of the pendulum, taking one oscillation as the equivalent of a kilometre, and got the number 'three'. He then proceeded to discover who had picked up the stones, putting the questions, Is it a man? Is it a woman? Is she pretty?, and arrived quickly at the answer.

Treyve was the manager of a large horticultural establishment near Moulins, and employed a number of workmen. I asked him one day what his staff thought of this activity. He laughed, and said they had good reason to beware of it, and related the following anecdote: 'You know the hedge which can be seen from my office window. One afternoon I noticed a workman getting over it; I at once thought he was going to visit one of the numerous cafés in the town. I took my pendulum and followed him. When he came back an hour later I sent for him and said; "You have been absent for an hour without leave and have visited such and such a café in the town. You ordered a litre of red wine. You invited two friends who were passing by, and you shared the wine between you." Frightened by this revelation, the workman fled, telling me I was a sorcerer. Since then no one has dared leave the workshop without permission.'

In this case, as before, Treyve had proceeded by successive interrogations, streets, cafés (he knew their names), various kinds of drink. The litre made him think that it could not have been drunk by one man, but must have been shared with friends.

Dr. Alfred Roux of Vichy, who is one of our best radiesthetic doctors, took up Radiesthesia as a result of the following event.

Being a great friend of J. Treyve, the latter made him a present of a pendulum, and explained how it should be used. Returning to his house, Dr. Roux found the letter of an unknown client announcing her arrival from Vichy. To amuse himself, Dr. Roux took the letter and the pendulum and then put a series of questions, such as a description of the lady, the state of her health, etc. He wrote several pages of questions and answers, which on the lady's arrival proved to be all, or nearly all, correct.

These are cases of two men exceptionally gifted. Here is the case of another whose success was intermittent.

Several years ago an old lady, a teacher in a Paris school, was staying with me for a few days. Hearing me talk of superpendulism, she asked for information. I made her a present of a pendulum, but told her that this was a branch of our art which I considered very unreliable, the prerogative of a few special individuals, and that I did not practise it myself. In fact, I gave her but small encouragement.

When she returned to her school, she met a person who

told her that she could claim possession of a tobacconist's shop provided she could prove that her father had been an official of a certain kind, but was unable to give any further information. The possibility of owning a tobacconist's shop was of outstanding importance to my old friend. She would be able to let it, and that would mean bread in her old age. But to whom was she to apply for information? She took her pendulum and a list of teachers at the school. The pendulum gyrated over the name of one of them. She met this mistress and explained her difficulty. The lady replied, 'How lucky! I have just had something to do with an affair of this kind. Go to such and such an official in such and such a Ministry.' My friend went there accordingly, and the official told her that the marriage certificate of her parents would be required. Here was a new difficulty, as she could not remember where her parents had been married. All she could recollect was that it was in a town in Alsace or Lorraine. She took a map of these provinces and presented the pendulum over the names of each of the towns. The pendulum gyrated for one of them. She wrote thither, and a few days later received the certificate—and in due course, the much-desired tobacconist's shop.

One could tell endless stories of this sort, I know hundreds of the most diverse kinds, for it is not only events in private life and the treatment of disease which are fitting subjects for the practice of superpendulism, but anything in the shape of a picture, a photo or a letter, any matter of uncertainty, anything which touches on human life and the affairs of man.

Is it all an illusion? No, in the majority of cases the stories are genuine, perhaps sometimes a little exaggerated and embellished, that is all one can say.

Should one attribute such results to chance? By no

means. Every successful case is the result of much research or questioning. One or two answers might be due to chance, but not an uninterrupted string of perhaps several dozen. We may well ask whether we are not dealing with one of the most extraordinary discoveries of all time—on a par with the atomic bomb!

Assuming that Superpendulism is the key to universal knowledge, there would be no secrets left either in politics or war. One could find out immediately the state of health of any potentate in Asia or elsewhere and what he is planning. One could spot the exact position of armies and fleets . . .

Is there a precedent for investigations of this kind? Ancient history and much of modern history give the answer 'Yes'. What were astrologers and diviners but the predecessors of our teleradiesthetists of to-day? The credit they enjoyed is a proof that they were not always wrong.

Nowadays there are numerous psychic circles in which operators known as mediums, clairvoyants, etc., get results of the same kind as those in which our teleradiesthetists excel. I think I can say that although these mediums, or most of them, are genuine professionals, they are easily surpassed by superpendulists, although they are mostly amateurs.

I knew the late Dr. Osty well, Director of the Institute of Metaphysics in Paris. One day he said to me, 'My students are good as regards the Past and the Present, but not the Future; unfortunately they have a rage for wanting to conduct their investigations in the Future.'

Do not the astounding results obtained depend on the fact that they are nearly always related to the Present and the Past? Even so limited, they would, if they were uniformly successful, be no less formidable in every sense of the word. I would have nothing to withdraw from what I have already said about Peace, War and Prosperity, for information on these heads concerns the Present.

Teleradiesthesia, therefore, deserves the most careful examination.

To begin with, it must be realised that it has spread in the most extraordinary manner. Practically unheard of in 1930, by 1940 it had become a matter of common knowledge. If it played no great part in the war of 1939, it is probably because its exponents were not sufficiently skilful or had not dared to come forward.

In the last twenty years I have collected an impressive list of facts, though it must be noted that however successful some of the operators were, there was a lack of regularity in their results—that is to say even the best of them cannot guarantee the certainty of being accurate. Up till now no way has been found of providing against failure, and this is particularly dangerous; it is all or nothing. We lack precise statistics. Certain good operators say that they get 70 or 80 per cent of successes; this is excellent, but needs to be verified.

One knows that really good performers are scarce, but so they are in music, painting and poetry. But this scarcity is no barrier to their immense usefulness. I have said above that up to now no way has been found of increasing the percentage of successes. Perhaps one might seek inspiration to this end from certain experiences of Abbé Mermet. He used to evaluate intellectual power by counting the oscillations of his pendulum. Could not the superpendulist, before working, verify with his instrument whether he is in a suitable psychic state? For instance, he knows that to undertake an investigation successfully he should provoke a coefficient of 15 to 20 in the pendulum.

If he only gives 5 or 6, he had better hold his hand for that day.

We cannot foresee the future of Teleradiesthesia, but it might be worth while to examine some of the conditions for its success.

Certain kinds of inquiry differ greatly from others, not only by reason of their nature, but in their need for exactness, or by the extent to which they lend themselves to control. Moreover, there are cases in which ambiguous information is better than none at all.

I will give some examples. A teleradiesthetic doctor always has the clinical examination at his disposal, in fact without it he cannot come to a final conclusion. Teleradiesthesia gives him information, which may be true, and which would otherwise have been unobtainable. For such a doctor, Teleradiesthesia is a clear asset. A police officer can likewise get useful information by superpendulism. In conducting his cases he often gets no little false information which he is not slow to verify. For him, a little false information more or less is of no importance, but if the pendulum shows him the right track, he has reason to be exultant. The future will perhaps bring up some pendulists of the style of Sherlock Holmes.

Certain considerations should be noted, amongst the most important being that one should never undertake inquiries of too personal a nature, towards which you are unable to adopt an entirely unprejudiced and indifferent attitude.

Like many others, I have practised Teleradiesthesia, but in spite of some successes I did not hesitate to abandon it because of the unreliability of the result in cases where I was myself concerned. I think, however, it will be useful to record two of these successes on account of their instructive nature.

The first was as follows:

One day a geologist friend sent me a plan of an area containing a large lake in the east of France, with a request to pass it on to a teleradiesthetist well known at the time, and ask him to mark on the plan the underground streams flowing into the lake. My geologist added that he was well acquainted with the course of the streams or water-bearing fissures. The teleradiesthetist returned me the plan, saying that he had not time to study it. Whilst I was writing my reply, it occurred to me that I might quickly run over the plan myself. I brought my pendulum over the plan, and, in accordance with the indications, drew three pencil lines on it. This took me about five minutes, whilst the teleradiesthetist had told me in his letter that it would have taken him some hours. I received an enthusiastic letter from the geologist by return of post telling me that my marks were correct, and sending another plan. In this case the result was pitiful. Evidently my mental attitude had changed. In the first case I had taken little trouble, in the second too much.

The other story is no less instructive. Someone who had heard tell of Joseph Treyve once asked me what my friend's method was. I made the following little speech, in a perhaps somewhat frivolous manner:

'Imagine, dear sir, that it is M. Treyve who is speaking to you this evening. I do not know your property; you tell me it is 200 kilometres from here. That is enough. At 10 metres to the north of your kitchen you will find an excellent place for digging a well. [Naturally I had taken my pendulum, and was copying Treyve by putting a series of questions, first about the kitchen and then about the well. I invented the whole thing, questions and answers, putting no bridle on my imagination.] You will come to a bed of clay, so many centimetres thick, a bed of limestone of so many centimetres, sand, then more clay, before reaching water, which will yield so many litres an hour. If you like, I will draw a little plan to show the site of the well more clearly in respect to the kitchen.'

I had finished my speech, but my interrogator, instead of being amused, had been looking at me for some time with an air of extreme bewilderment. 'But, my dear sir,' he said, 'what you have just said is absolutely true. I had not told you that I had had a well dug and that everything happened just as you have stated.' I must confess that I was no less stupefied than he was. Here was a correct result, achieved without the remotest expectation of success.

It is probably because this condition is entirely lacking that hitherto good results have not been obtained at competitions in this subject. Yet an investigation carried out by team work would be extremely useful if it could be arranged.

It is pretty certain that if three or four qualified operators arrived at the same results the probability of accuracy would be greatly increased. Let us hope that the coming years will admit of such work being carried out by teams, for this seems to be the principal aim which teleradiesthetists should pursue.

It remains to discuss what the nature of this phenomenon of Teleradiesthesia or Superpendulism really is.

At first it was thought that Teleradiesthesia proper was a wave phenomenon, but obvious difficulties were soon apparent. One could not seriously speak of 'waves of the Past'. Even regarding the Present, the problem was insurmountable for anyone who had some understanding of 'Wireless'. Several years before the war of 1939 any physical theory of Teleradiesthesia had been abandoned, and nothing but Empiricism was left. To connect

Teleradiesthesia with Metaphysics is like ascribing one unknown to another, or at least to one still under discussion.

Perhaps a reference to the manuals of classical Philosophy in use at Universities would not be out of place. In them there is a vast amount of matter which is indisputable from a scientific point of view and has long been accepted officially. In our textbooks there is always a chapter on Intuition, where the subject is somewhat inadequately treated. Might we not assimilate its contents and add something on our own account?

Intuition is defined as 'The immediate and complete cognition of any object or truth'. One might say, 'Perception without reasoning'. As this is a subject with which few of my readers are likely to be familiar, I will enlarge on it a little.

Intuition is the heading of a chapter on Philosophy, a somewhat inadequate one, for in two large volumes of an enormous work on Philosophy now lying before me, only two pages are devoted to the subject. In the last few years, however, Bergson has again drawn attention to Intuition, at a time when, in spite of its recognition in the most remote times and the important part it plays in Psychology, it appeared to be wellnigh forgotten.

Bergson was one of those rare philosophers of the first rank who have recognised that which is called the Supernormal, as witness his famous address to the Society for Psychical Research in London. Intuition, it would seem, is destined to become the connecting link between the ancient and modern philosophical knowledge.

It is certain that until quite recent times so-called divination, whether deriving from cards, coffee-grounds, crystal balls, clairvoyance, etc., was considered to be of supernatural origin. People were inclined to class it amongst the Occult Sciences; sometimes it was even attributed to Spirits. A first forward step was made with the foundation of Psychical Societies, by the recognition of its purely human origin.

A second step seems to have been made in regarding Divination as less strange and exceptional than it was previously held to be, and in connecting it with the old conception of Intuition which is universally accepted. Let Teleradiesthesia find a place there, and other Sciences, now on the verge of recognition, will not be slow to follow. And so perhaps a little light will be shed in places which have till now been considered all too dark.

We know that we have Intuition of First Principles of metaphysical origin, Identity, Causality, Teleology, Substance. There is no plausible reason why there should not be other forms of Intuition.

It is a fact of everyday experience that ideas come to us which arise in our mind without reasoning, and bring the solution of some problem or other with which we have been preoccupied.

It is recognised that certain people have considerable power of intuition and derive much good therefrom. Perhaps it may be regarded as the highest of our faculties.

Till now Intuition has always been regarded as spontaneous, and not to be acquired by training. Is this true? Recent experiences with the pendulum tend to prove otherwise. Many of our operators profess to have progressed since they began, though most of them have never bothered to adopt any particular order or method in their work.

It should be possible to devise a progressive and systematic course of training in Superpendulism which might well give more consistent results than have been obtained hitherto.

It seems easier to exercise Intuition to good effect in matters of which all the elements are already known to us than in respect to things of which we know nothing.

To continue, I think we can consider it accepted that Teleradiesthesia should be regarded as a form of Intuition. No other alternative seems possible. Nevertheless, whether Intuition be spontaneous or the result of training, it is impossible to lay down in the present state of human knowledge the process by which it works.

When it is a question of professional Intuition—if one can so call it—one understands, or thinks one understands, a little, for generally it concerns new connections between known elements; but what is to be said of the sudden flashes of knowledge on matters hitherto quite unknown, as in most of the examples I have given? It is as if our mind had at its disposal an astounding faculty of direct knowledge, which we have not yet learnt to use. Shall we ever do so? The secret is buried in the Future. In any case, the method of Teleradiesthesia seems to have produced in a very short time results superior to other methods of divination. It seems capable of reconciliation with certain ideas formerly held by Philosophy, and for this reason it deserves to be encouraged and to be taken seriously.

A last question remains to be examined. Is there anything in common between Radiesthesia proper and Teleradiesthesia, apart from the use of similar instruments? I readily admit that one can attempt to solve radiesthetic problems by teleradiesthetic methods in accordance with the old proverb, '*Qui peut le plus, peut le moins.*' Obviously, one cannot proceed on the ground as if one were on a large map, and put oneself a number of rapid questions.

But compare the two processes attentively. In the first place, Radiesthesia belongs to the Philosophy of Sensa-

tion, as indeed its name indicates, and Teleradiesthesia
to that of Intuition.   They are two entirely distinct, if not
actually opposed faculties, seeing that Intuition by
definition dispenses with Sensation.   It is in this sense that
in Philosophy one speaks in the first case of sensuous, and
in the second of extra-sensuous knowledge.

But it may be objected that in Teleradiesthesia one
registers the movements of the pendulum.   Are these not
indices of the Sensations?   In no way.   When its movements are analysed, it can be seen that they might as well
not have taken place.   They are merely an aid designed
to elicit the answer.   Certain operators, amongst them
M. Discry, President of the International Centre for the
Scientific Study of Radiesthesia and of the Academy of
Radiesthetic Sciences of Belgium, have ascertained that
the answer is received in the mind before the pendulum
begins to move.   I have known others who, after having
started with the pendulum rather like an acrobat using a
balancing pole, have abandoned it, or at least use it only
as a safeguard.

The radiesthetist in his work takes into account Space,
Time and Matter.   His action is very limited, being confined to his immediate surroundings and to the Present.
In spite of the methods of check which I have described,
one can be sure that he will refuse in advance any experiment which seems to him at first sight to depart from the
normal limits of the Sensations.   He tries to conform to the
methods and usages of orthodox science, so as to gain
recognition for himself and for his craft.

The teleradiesthetist, on the other hand, will take no
heed of Space, Time and Matter and is but little disturbed
by the opinions of scientists.   In his case Sensations do
not apply, as their laws have been deliberately excluded.

To conclude, Teleradiesthesia during the period between

the two wars has enjoyed a time of widespread popularity. By reason of its extra-sensuous nature, it has met with opposition in scientific circles, but it has found ample compensation in the attention paid it by immense crowds, attracted by the element of the marvellous. Moreover, it has had the luck of owing its inception to an important group of operators of the first rank who were often excellent lecturers. Let us hope that its luck will continue, and that the gaps made by death in the ranks of its exponents will be quickly filled. Its final success will depend in large measure on the continuation of its popularity.

The position of Radiesthesia proper, on the contrary, is quite different. If during the period of which we have spoken it has been largely eclipsed by its rival to the extent that its very existence was threatened, it has none the less succeeded in surviving, as witness the publication of this book.

Its field of action is obviously much more restricted than that of Teleradiesthesia; its presentation to an audience is less likely to cause enthusiasm, whilst its practitioners are less known and do not enjoy the same prestige as do superpendulists.

However, Radiesthesia is based firmly on Sensation, and is therefore within the classic domain of Normal Consciousness. Consequently it advances no claims at which the most meticulous scientist could take offence, provided he take the trouble to listen to reason and to lay aside his prejudices. Little by little these will disappear. That which is represented as merely an auxiliary method cannot be indefinitely rejected.

It can be seen then that the respective positions of Radiesthesia and Teleradiesthesia are, and must be, entirely different. They belong to different chapters of Philosophy, do not appeal to the same intelligences, nor do they serve the same ends. To confuse the two can in the end only prejudice both. Better that they should part company in friendly fashion and follow each its own road.

However, in present circumstances, and in accordance with the old proverb 'Union makes Strength', it would be as well that this separation be effected in a manner advantageous to both. I would be ready to see it limited to the formation of two groups in one existing association, each pursuing its own course.

Often enough dissension occurs in consequence of profound philosophical disagreement. We do not run that risk, seeing that the one branch refers to one chapter and the other to another chapter of a same Philosophy.

I do not know what the future of Teleradiesthesia will be and whether the age-long problem of Divination will ever be solved even in its application to the Present. We can but welcome those who wish to indulge in this new application of the pendulum.

If the results are not commensurate with their hopes, they can always abandon their ambitious experiments and resume the more modest but more certain practice of genuine Radiesthesia. This is another reason why radiesthetists and teleradiesthetists, whilst preserving their independence and refraining from mutual criticism, should continue to be members of the same societies.

INDEX

Accords, 61–2
Agricultural Radiesthesia, x, 57–64
Alimentary Radiesthesia, 45–50
Ampère, A. M., 2, 6
Analysis, 40, 41, 49, 59
Antenna, use of arm as, 8, 22, 33, 34, 35, 41, 63
Association des Amis de la Radies-thésie, 3
Atomic weights, 26
Automatic adjustment of pendulum, 35–6, 41

Balance, method of, 41, 59
Barrett, Sir William, ix
Beausoleil, Baron de, 1, 19
Bergson, Henri, 75
Besterman, Theodore, ix
Bouly, Abbé, 3, 12, 19, 23, 41, 51
British Society of Dowsers, 3

Causes of reactions, 9–10, 17
Cavities, 43
Chastelet, Jean du, 1
Check, methods of, 8–9, 16, 22–4, 34
Chevreul, M. E., 2, 6
Clay, effect of, 21, 34
Coal, 44
Cody, Pierre, 17, 38, 54, 55
Coefficients, method of, 46–7, 54
Coloured screens, 52–3
Colours, method of, 14, 26–8, 41, 63–4; author's tables of, 27, 28
Comment J'Opère, 65
Congresses, 3, 55, 56
Cooking, 49

Depth, estimation of, 16, 32–4, 36
Descartes, René, 2

Diagnosis, medical, 51–2
Discry, Georges, 59
Divination, 6, 32, 75, 76
Divining Rod, The, ix
Doctors and teleradiesthesia, 72
Dowsing, 26

Electrified patches of ground, 36, 62
Electroscope, 55
Elements of Mineralogy, 39
'Eyes closed', check of, 2, 6, 8, 11, 23

Ferran, Abbé, 43
Fertilisers, 60, 61
Field, 'direction' of, 14, 15, 53, 59
Fields, method of, 14–16, 17, 58
Fissures, 34, 41, 42, 54, 55
'Following' the pendulum, 22, 42, 60
Foods, testing of, ix, xi, 46–7, 58
Franklin, T. Bedford, ix, 17
Fundamental ray, 15

Geology, books on, ix, 29, 39, 41, 57
Gerboin, Antoine, 2

Halifax, Lord, 2
Homeopathy, 54
Human products, use of, 52

Injurious rays, 54–6, 58
Instrumental verification, 17, 18, 23, 37, 55
Intersection of streams, 34, 62

81

Introduction to Geology, An, 29
Intuition, 75–80

La Chronique des Sourciers, 17
La Découverte des Eaux Minérales de Château-Thierry, 1
La Physique Occulte, 1
La Restitution de Pluton, 1
La Véritable Déclaration des Mines de France, 1
Le Sourcier Moderne, vii, 45, 57
Liége, Congress at, 3
Lightning, 62
Linden, D. W., 2

Maby, J. Cecil, ix, 9, 17, 23, 36, 37, 55
Mager, Henri, ix, 3, 26, 65
Magnet, use of, 32, 33, 40
Manures, 60
Maps, method of dowsing on, 66
Martin, Abel Ernest, 51, 54
Mass, estimation of, 16
Medical Radiesthesia, 3, 51–6
Meridian Plane, method of, 19, 20–2, 46, 47
Mermet, Abbé, 24, 51, 53, 65, 71
Metals, 40
Minerals, 39, 41
Modern Dowser, The, vii

Non-metals, 40

Oil, 44
Ores, 41
Osty, Dr., 70

Pendulum, how to make, 4; advantages of, 4, 37; hollow, 5, 40, 41, 42, 60; adjustment of, 6–9, 30, 31, 35–6, 39, 40, 62, 64; heavy, 36

Photographic verification, 37–8, 55
Photos, method of dowsing on, 66
Physics of the Divining Rod, The, ix, 17
Plants, chemical content of, 49, 61
Pohl, Baron von, 54
Pollution, 34
Potability, 34

Radiesthesia, defined, 12–3; field of application, 12–3
Radiesthésie, origin of word, 12
Radioactive soils, 46
Raistrick, A., 29
Ravat, M., 62
Regnault, Dr. Jules, 54
Remedies, 53–4
Ritter, J. G., 2
Rod, how to make, 10; how to hold, 11, 17; use of, 19, 36, 43, 50
Roux, Dr. Alfred, 68
Rutley, F., 39

Samples, method of, 14, 19–20, 26, 35, 40, 59, 60, 61
Schools, 29, 45, 48
Screening, effect of, 53
Seeds, 59
Selige, Dr. Adolph, 45
'Series', method of, 14, 24–6, 35, 40, 41; author's tables of, 25, 63
'Sheets' of water, 30
Society for Psychical Research, 75
Solar Plane, method of, 19, 20–2, 40, 47, 61
Springs of water, 30
Streams, 34–6; superimposed, 34–5; hot and mineral, 35–6
Superpendulism, *see* Teleradiesthesia

Teach Yourself Geology, 29
Teleradiesthesia, nature of, 74–80; vii, 53, 65–80
Téléradiésthie, invention of word, 65
Three letters on Mining and Smelting, 2

Treyve, Joseph, 65–8, 73
Trinder, Captain W. H., 26
Tristan, Comte de, 2, 51
Trueman, A. E., 29

Vallemont, Abbé de, (Le Lorrain), 1
Valuables, 43
Vines, 62

Viré, Armand, 3

Water Diviners and their Methods, ix
Water Divining, ix
Water, dowsing for, 29–38; under
  pressure, 36, 43
Wells, 31, 57

Yield, estimation of, 16, 21–32, 34